the rainbow bird

MARGARET WAY

the rainbow bird

HARLEQUIN BOOKS
toronto-winnipeg

CHAPTER ONE

HE was there when she got back to the flat: lounging at the top of the stairs. Tall, mercurial, very lean, young man style, good shoulders, a shining blond, one hand thrust through his curls, the other pushed in his pocket, a wry, laconic grin on his mobile mouth.

'Hi there, Red! Didn't think a Benedict would take defeat that easily?'

She hesitated for a moment, staring upwards, caught in the rigor of surprise, then she recovered. She came on up the stairs almost at an impatient rush.

'Joel! See here, I really *do* have a dinner date!' Her voice was vital, attractive, oddly inflected.

'Break it!' He stood watching her with a kind of narcotic satisfaction, fascinated by her quiet, silky movements. He ran a forefinger down the straight line of his nose and the laconic grin broke up. He looked older, harder, that much used to having his own way, looking her straight in the eyes, his eyebrows raised quizzically.

'No chance!' His impudence made her feel physically breathless. She swept past him, barely reaching his shoulder, slender as a tulip with a rare co-ordination of movement.

'Who's it with?' He gave a low chuckle and whisked the key out of her hand with astonishing speed, inserting it in the lock and turning it deftly. His smile was back, hovering near the edge of laughter.

'Well?'

She tossed back her hair and flashed him a funny little glance, half irritation, half surrender. His swift, casual movement seemed a mixture of defiance and ostentation to her. Her voice sank a little as if she was trying to keep it under control.

'You'd always rate an A for effort, Joel Benedict. I wasn't fooling. I really do have a dinner engagement. A client, a soap manufacturer's agent. Just a routine coverage.' Her large eyes, an intensely feminine feature of her face, flicked upwards, catching his sceptical grin. 'A business matter, pure and simple!'

He gave his sardonic smile again and she burst out in irritation.

'Damn it, Joel! Why am I bothering explaining?'

'Why, indeed! our hot shot little career woman!' He raised an expressive eyebrow opening the door, holding it with a long arm, eyes mocking, hazel, gold-flecked.

'Anything but! Some days I think I'm in the dreariest business in the world!' She swept past him, small poised head averted; a satiny ribbon of hair, restless with a hundred glistening highlights.

Odd-coloured hair, he mused, irresistibly caught. Like the shiny bronzed leaf of a rose. His eyes flickered beyond her to the apartment. It was the first time he had ever been inside. It couldn't have proclaimed more clearly its owner; vibrant, contemporary beauty, a creamy pale ground glowing with colour accents, scorning the usual fripperies but very feminine. An alluring impression! He knew she worked for a big advertising agency. Fashion, that was her game. An insane occupation, she might call it, but she was very good at it, so *he* heard, and obviously it paid well.

Paige shot him a curious look, her feathery dark

brows slanting upwards at his frankly inquisitive expression.

'Is there something you want to talk over, Joel?'

He grinned back at her, not a bit abashed. 'It's not that!'

'Then what is it? I warn you, I'm in an awful rush.'

His eyes held hers; gentle, but in the gentleness something inflexible. 'I just wanted to see you, that's all!'

'Oh, come now, Joel!' Her voice contrived to be reproachful yet caressingly amused.

'Yes, really!'

There was a sharp little silence and she waited resignedly.

'I'm crazy about you, Red. That's why!' He walked across to the mantelpiece and leant an elbow on it, fiery pride in his face. 'Just plain crazy, God help me!' He was watching her closely, seeing the little shock wave that rocked her, the widening eyes. Colour swept into her face, making it breathtakingly lovely, lending it a kind of wild rose abandonment.

'Oh, lord!' he said softly, walking slowly towards her. 'Do I really have to tell you? Can't you guess I go all weak at the knees just to see you? Like a newborn colt!'

'Joel!' She gave a funny, husky little gurgle deep in her throat, taking him by surprise. Her lips were half parted, a dreamy sweetness in her eyes. Recklessly he reached for her, sliding his hand into the small of her back, to pull her towards him. She recoiled like a startled fawn, but he wouldn't let her go. His long, strong arms encircled her, using his strength for mastery. He needed that kiss. She opened her mouth to protest, but he gave her no chance. The last rays of sunlight glanced off his blond head as he found her mouth, quick and hard and very real with a single-minded determination and ardour. The pale skin of her throat was flawless and he trailed his mouth over it to where a pulse beat heavily.

'There they go again,' he whispered, 'a shower of coloured lights! What do you do to me, girl?'

Her eyes opened and flickered into his and her head snapped back like a rose in a high wind. There was an ardent heat in his strong arms, a brilliant snap in his eyes. She leaned back against his arms, trying to speak lightly.

'For someone just in from the sandhills, you're a very fast mover. Too fast, I find myself thinking. I'm not ready for all this, Joel!'

There was a taut pain where he held her. His hand snaked out and brushed her hair from her cheek with a markedly possessive gesture. The closeness of her was exquisite. So much so he was almost frightened of his feelings.

'Don't bawl me out, honey,' he said carefully. 'A Benedict will stand only so much!'

She twisted away, bright as a firefly, her smile implying a certain criticism.

'A Benedict! Big deal! One of our all-powerful cattle barons. Look at it this way, Joel my lad, what you know about fashion wouldn't amount to a hill of beans!'

His long mobile mouth curved, glancing at her out of the corner of his eye. 'I like what *you're* wearing, honey chile. Even without your face you'd still turn a man's head!'

'Thank you for that, anyway.' She turned away and switched on a lamp. It arced over her bent head flashing out all its incipient reds and ambers. 'I guess you've got the sweet kind of gall to win any number of women, Joel Benedict. But not me. *I* have to chase you.'

His high spirits dipped to a kind of whimsical humour. 'No pretty girl should be on her own,' he stressed in a mild, patient way, as if he had to explain a lot of things to a lot of people.

'Sometimes she prefers it,' she pointed out gently.

'Then she doesn't know any better. What are you running away from, Red?'

Her heart seemed to be thudding in her chest. The silence in the room was almost electric. 'I'm not running at all!' she said firmly, nearly convincing herself.

'Are you sure of that?' His hazel eyes glinted and she picked up a book and closed it with a snap.

'Joel dear, I'm trying to be patient, but I must shower and change. My date is calling for me in little over an hour.'

'Can't I wait here?' He held her eyes with a kind of gay charm that had worked very well in the past. 'I'll talk to you while you're dressing. I promise you I'll be no bother.' His eyes sparkled ironically with a daredevil glitter and she nibbled on her underlip.

There was a kind of lustre about him, a young, healthy shine to his eyes, his skin and his hair. He didn't look like a cattle man at all but a handsome, 'with-it', highly eligible young man about town. What was the matter with her? She sighed heavily. There wasn't a girl in her right mind who'd turn down Joel

Benedict, even without the fabled Benedict assets. There weren't too many people in the fair State of Queensland who hadn't read the saga of John Bateman Benedict – 'Big John' Benedict, the young English adventurer, who, by a rare combination of luck, vision, drive and ambition, rose to be one of the big cattle kings with a chain of stations across the top half of the continent.

Thousands of miles of Central and South-Western Queensland and into the Territory were 'Benedict country' with Benedict men swarming all over the Outback; station managers, agents, drovers, stockmen, outriders. The boundaries of the old Benedict empire had receded with sub-division, but there was still enough of it to be lit up with neon.

Paige stood there staring at Joel's young, self-revealing face. If she remembered correctly, 'Big John's' eldest son, 'Duke' Benedict, Joel's father, was killed in some hair-raising exploit up in the Top End. She couldn't remember the exact details, but it was something to do with a crocodile shoot, the big salt water variety. Joel rarely mentioned his family. He had a mother, a brother and a sister, and that piece of information had only been contributed in passing. It seemed when Joel was in the city, he was bent on forgetting 'Koombala', the old aboriginal name for Benedict Downs. She knew a fleeting curiosity to see it. These immense pastoral holdings, almost empires within themselves, had a kind of romantic awe for the 'fringe dwellers', the city dwellers of the coastline. Benedict Downs, one of the greatest of them all, exerted a powerful influence on the Australian cattle industry not only because of its tremendous size and prime cattle, but because of its colourful history, its remoteness, and the aura of the name, 'Big John' Benedict, one of the great pioneers of the Big Country, the Back of Beyond where there were no fences and a man could make a name and fortune.

Paige stood in the centre of the room, her jumbled emotions showing on her face. The atmosphere subtly changed. Joel turned about, breathed a deep sigh, then flopped down on the sofa, long legs stretched out in front of him, slightly awkward.

'The siege has begun!' he said tritely. 'And if you're not pleased with yourself, then you damn well ought to be!'

'You can't count on anything in this world!' she pointed out dryly, wondering how long he proposed to settle there.

He only smiled. 'You and your magic!' he grinned mischievously, making her feel out of her depth. Dealing with Joel was like riding the tiger. He had an untamed quality about him for all his sophisticated veneer. Perhaps it was his environment, the tremendous sense of space and freedom. Whatever it was, it put him markedly apart from any other young man she had known. His attitude was flippant, his manner relaxed, but his eyes, had she been watching, were lost and yearning. Her beauty seemed to mock him – the cool grace, that maddening little air of detachment. He wanted to know her shape and texture, not only the tantalizing taste of her mouth, the silken warmth of her hair, the satiny skin and fragile neck, the sweet scent of innocence. It was a scarcely endurable pain to be really in love for the first time. Something very strange was happening to him, a knot of pleasure and pain that was

13

blinding. He stretched and linked his hands behind his head with the sketchiest pretence at casualness.

Her eyes reminded him of the waterlilies on the billabong back home – a kind of ash violet or hyacinth or whatever! Eyes a man could drown in. He'd only known her three weeks, but he wanted her, badly. And he meant to have her. Nothing would stop him this time. Nothing and no one! Not even Ty, the man himself, Crown Prince to the Empire. Good old Ty! It was no coincidence that he fitted the frame predestined for him, a man in the same stamp as his grandfather, with the same force and direction. A shooting star to soar across the brilliant sky of Koombala. And good luck to him, Joel thought cynically. He had no head at all for crowning achievements. Some days in bitter anger he cursed the fact that he was the second son, at other times he realized it was right and better so. Strong men had pioneered the Outback, men who cared little for convention, untameable men who wrested from a primeval earth what they wanted and devil take anyone who stood in their way. Ty was that kind of man. He wasn't. It didn't make him less of a man, just different.

He had a sharp mental picture of his stepbrother. Ty, tall and rangy, Indian dark, eyes all the greens of the grasslands, from the clear shimmering colour of the open savannahs to the cabuchon glitter of the secretive rock pools. Thirty-five and he'd never married, though he'd had more than his share of women in three States – society dolls mostly, toppling over themselves to pull off a major matrimonial prize, foolishly imagining they could separate the man from the land for at least part of the time. Some hope! Ty and Koombala were one.

14

Ty was in no hurry to take a wife. No one pushed Ty, like they pushed Joel. Breathing quickly, Joel bent over and lit a cigarette trying to settle himself. It was no easy thing to live in a man's shadow and damned difficult for him. He loved and admired his stepbrother, but his deep-driven resentment was only half realized. Strange how Ty haunted the mind's eye. It was almost a shock to realize he was only mortal and would one day have to die just as his grandfather would die. In the meantime Ty was Ty the big wheel, the cattle baron, head of the Benedict organization now that their grandfather had virtually retired. His image persisted.

Ty, rocking gently in high leather boots, silver trappings exploding in the sunlight, whistling tunelessly through his teeth, silver grey Stetson tipped over one eye, the cool, competent professional, waiting to break in the best of the range-bred thoroughbreds, plumes flying spirit and independence flashing from their white-ringed eyes; Tracey and Di sitting on the fence in a frenzy of sun and excitement shouting encouragements, along with the stock boys who loved nothing better than a display of superb horsemanship, coupled with just that much showmanship to keep the girls entertained. It never occurred to any of them that the Boss could break his neck or a lot worse. But Ty never faltered, never rode a horse to the limit, never pushed a victory. He loved his horses and bred the best.

What would Paige think of him? Better not dwell on it. They'd have precious little time together. He'd make certain of that! Still, it wouldn't be easy, this task he had set himself. Yet everything he had ever desired seemed to crystallize into wanting this one girl ...

Paige. And even she might prove difficult! She had a life of her own in the city, success of a kind. There was a delicate strength to her face like a very fine cameo, a captivating cleft to her chin, and it wasn't there for nothing, of that he was sure. There was fire under that limpid exterior, a redhead's natural volatility. Non-chalantly he glanced up and caught that hyacinth gaze and his careful restraint disintegrated.

'Paige!' He said her name softly, intensely, as if in a dream.

For a moment she felt incapable of constructive thought. 'I might have known,' she said almost desperately, thinking her thoughts aloud. 'Something like this was bound to happen. You're so very impulsive, so headstrong, Joel!'

He spread his hands, lean, long-fingered. 'Is it so very bad? My loving you, I mean?'

'It could be!' Now why did she say that? She tried to shake off a sense of alarm, talking more to herself than to him, reacting to that look of helpless vulnerability like a change of personality, for normally Joel Benedict was a very arrogant young man born to great wealth and complete independence. It gave one a queer feeling to have that much power. Almost for a moment she was afraid.

He got up and came over to her and held her shoulders, surveying her with great gravity out of his long hazel eyes.

'This is preordained, Paige. I know it.'

She fought down an inexplicable rush of temper. He was forcing the situation, taking so very much for granted – charging ahead like the West to be won, yet he attracted her far more than anyone she had ever met. What was it she expected out of life . . . of love? A shaft of lightning. A bolt from the blue to shrivel her in its radiance! This is it! My man! It rarely happened like that. She was a hopeless romantic, aching for a great love, and it was so naïve, completely unrealistic. Not for her the fire and the anguish, the dangerous burning sweetness. She would have to come to terms with her nature, and Joel was very, very attractive. What did she want? A demi-god?

He shook her gently. 'What is it, Red?' A cool fanaticism had settled on him. She would never get away.

'Nothing!' she moved her head fretfully from side to side. 'I just feel a little strange, that's all. You're a very disturbing element about the place – and *must* you use that ridiculous nickname?'

'I could make it Rose-Red!' he smiled, and slipped a hand under her hair, caressing the nape of her neck, losing himself in the scent and sensation of her. 'Paige, honey, you tear me apart!' His lips smiled, but his eyes were dead sober.

Her expression warned him, the telltale sweep of colour that stained her creamy skin. She was the possessor of an enviable pigmentation; a natural russet-head whom the sun loved. So much the better, he thought. Koombala was no place for a problem complexion. He tried to isolate what it was about her that made him want to look and look and never get tired. Tracey, in a completely opposite fashion, was almost as eye-catching, her features more classic, yet the irregular pitch of Paige's fine dark brows, the velvety beauty spot at the corner of her mouth, were oddly entrancing.

'Please, Joel!' she said very quickly, pushing against his chest. 'You don't know your own strength. You're hurting me.'

He released her with a quick 'sorry!' his long fingers leaving marks on her soft flesh. She was temperamental, his rose-bronze beauty, but he had no objection to a filly with spirit. She needed gentling but plenty of control. He moved away across the room, with lazy economical movements.

'You care for me more than a little, Red. I'm not that much of a fool.'

His ears were faintly pointed, set close to his head, giving him a dashing, golden satyr look. She couldn't deny it, her voice softening.

'I do like you, Joel, very much. Or rather, I like what I see and the little I've heard, but I scarcely know the real you.'

'That's easily remedied!' His smile was dazzling, alive with a passionate certainty. 'Come back with me to the Big Country. See it for yourself. It'd be no loss even in the fashion business. The colours on Koombala have to be seen to be believed. The brilliance of the earth and the sky, the fiery rose of the sandhills, the hourly colour changes that would drive an artist wild. You'd love it! An assault on the senses. Besides, Benedict Downs is a kinda showplace,' he drawled, as if that alone would clinch all argument, a masterly understatement.

Paige stood staring at him without speaking. Most girls he knew would topple over backwards at such an invitation, yet Paige stood staring with wide impersonal eyes, as if seeking the elemental truth of him.

'I could scarcely go visiting without an invitation

from your mother,' she pointed out finally, with no other thought in her head than to put him off.

'And what if you had one?' he shot back at her, beating his fingers restlessly on the coffee table, like drum-roll. Her beautiful mouth was amused. She looked at him rather wryly, trying to gauge just how serious he was.

'I might reconsider,' she said lightly, purposely offhand. 'And now, Joel Benedict of Koombala, Benedict Downs – lovely name – I'm going to get dressed. You go your way. I'll go mine. There are some magazines on the stand, the stereo in the corner. Make yourself a drink. There's quite a selection in the cabinet over there. Not for private consumption, in case you're wondering. Ice in the fridge.'

'Terrific!' he responded happily. He pulled off his jacket and rummaged in the pockets for his cigarettes. He lit one, smiling at his shaking hand. 'Go right ahead. I'll be happy here. Besides, I want to che.. 'I this soap manufacturer of yours.'

'Soap manufacturer's *agent*,' she corrected, and waved pale, slender fingers over her shoulder.

'What are you wearing?' he called after her lazily, without moving, his eyes very bright.

'You'll see!'

He gave a long luxurious sigh. 'Perfect!'

Her date arrived ten minutes early. Joel heard his voice in the hall, a pleasantly affected drawl. It gave him a jarring sensation.

'Paige darling! You look gorgeous. Absolutely fab! A witching sight, and that was a fantastic job you did on Masterton. Prestige exposure. A total success. Thank you from the bottom of my heart.'

There was a small loaded silence and Joel strolled out into it, six feet two, lanky lean, a deceptively amiable gleam in his eye. No sense in giving the competition heaven-sent opportunties. Paige appeared none the worse for a discreet kiss of homage, an enormous sheaf of tea roses, exquisitely tinted, over her arm.

She looked up and smiled with complete impartiality, introducing the two men with practised charm and a certain inward anxiety, fairly certain Joel would be haunted by a green-eyed devil, now and then. Closer the mark than she ever imagined.

'Joel Benedict . . . Mark Ridgway!'

The two men shook hands. 'Benedict? Now isn't that something! No relation to *the* Benedict of Benedict Downs?' Ridgway was enthusing, his smallish, shrewd eyes snapping with interest.

Joel nodded briefly. 'I guess you could mean my grandfather or my brother.'

'Your brother, I'd say,' Ridgway supplied pleasantly. 'I met him about eighteen months ago. He was guest speaker at our big Rotary convention. Handsome devil, isn't he? *And* a damn good speaker. Terrific natural authority. A real man's man. I'd never have picked him for your brother – different colouring and all,' he hastened to tack on, misliking the young fellow's expression.

The knife turned in an old wound, though these days he didn't bleed so easily. 'Ty's my *stepbrother*,' Joel pointed out very precisely for a voice with a natural drawl. 'Head of the Benedict empire by divine edict – the old man's, to be exact.'

'Is that so!' Ridgway stole a look at the young man sideways. It sounded like that handsome straight nose was slightly out of joint. But Joel wasn't looking at him at all. He was looking at Paige, and Ridgway couldn't blame him. Paige Norton was a delectable young creature, and better still had brains – *and* if his eyes weren't deceiving him she had Joel Benedict tied up in knots.

She was wearing an evening maxi with long sleeves and a low neckline – ultra-chic, Joel supposed, but it was a funny drab colour, a kind of coffee brown, yet it pointed up her skin and hair in the most flagrant fashion. He decided then and there that he wasn't even on the fringe of the glamour world. He would never have picked that colour for her, yet he had to admit it packed a powerful punch. Tracey, now, stuck slavishly to blue, having read once in a magazine that it was a man's favourite colour. Poor old Tracy! His mouth twitched involuntarily, as it always did when he thought of Tracey Ord, his mother's godchild, daughter of her dearest friend, orphaned at twelve and brought up on Koombala by his mother. Tracey, he had long since concluded, was a 'hornery little critter', but she was as sweet as run honey with Ty.

Damn Ty! Joel thought savagely. There wasn't a single situation he didn't intrude on. But not this one. No, sir! His mother could look Paige over, get to know her future daughter-in-law, then wham! a quick trip back to the city, the legal walk taken, then he and Paige could settle to anything – even a life in the shimmering sun-scorched plains of the South-West. Perhaps Ty would let him have a station of his own, less remote, nearer the rolling Central Downs. He could put in a manager and spend half his time on the coast. What was the sense in having money if you couldn't spend it? Besides, a hot-house rose like Paige

21

would wilt in the Outback. Or would she? She was still an enigma to him, but so desirable it hurt. He was a damn fool to propose taking her home at all. Not with Ty around. Not within the orbit of that dark vitality. Ty, the undisputed local lord of creation. But his mother would be hurt and angered, and hurting his mother wasn't one of Joel's failings.

Paige turned away to put the roses in water and the two men were left alone for a few moments, neither entirely comfortable, for Joel's terse remark had created a constraint. Ridgway asked a few questions about life among the sandhills, drought, overstocking in good times, touched briefly on 'one helluva' trip he had made to the Alice and received such laconic answers he finally gave up. It was plain to see Joel Benedict was growing more morose by the minute – and not only morose, but sulky, outdone. An arrogant young hot-head, Ridgway concluded. That blond, handsome face could if it wished look decidedly unpleasant. Joel Benedict was clearly used to having his own way, yet Ridgway couldn't imagine anyone putting anything across the big fellow, the stepbrother. What was his Christian name again? Something unusual. Tyrone, that was it! Ty Benedict. A man to contend with, even for this young feller-me-lad with his bright hazel eyes and Lucifer tilt to the head. These cattle barons. God damn them, Ridgway thought, irritated and envious. There was no need for them to act as if the whole damn country belonged to them. One thing was certain, and he derived a kind of waspish satisfaction from it, lanky lean blondie here was the boy, but the big fellow, Ty, was the man. Pity young Paige if she ever got caught between the two of them!

CHAPTER TWO

It was a pitiless country. God, how pitiless! Would she ever get used to the dust and the heat, the sun-ravaged landscape? Across the airstrip, skirmishing little dust devils danced and darted in erratic spirals, breathing their fiery furnace breath; whirlwinds of red dust, dry grass and brittle leaves, filtering the atmosphere, colouring the sunlight, permeating body and mind. Paige bit her lip, filled with the queer melancholy of the country, a melancholy she could not understand. The brown immensity of this ancient land was terrifying to her, as it must have been to the explorers it claimed. But neither they nor she could resist the force of it, the dignity and the sadness.

She was rather pale, little points of moisture glittering on her forehead, at the roots of her hair. She slipped a finger under her sunglasses, troubled by trickles of perspiration under her eyes. It was a breathless day of aching heat; a torrid sky, piled high on the western horizon with great rainbow-hued clouds, silver and saffron and purple, billowing like an atomic mushroom, the sky overhead glowing, fluorescent, a strange atmospheric effect of the approaching dust storm. She moistened her dry lips with the tip of her tongue. The whole world seemed to be glaring at her. What on earth had she let herself in for?

A thousand miles away the lush eastern seaboard had burst into an urgent ecstasy of spring, a sensuous multi-coloured fantasy of tropical density. Out here the winter rains had failed and now the only vital thing was the sun ... the cruel and beautiful mirage; the tormenting silver-blue demon, that leapt like a flame over the drought-conquered land. Only two days ago she had revelled in the flower-scented warmth of home. Now this! Her body shivered in its thin covering, exposed to the keenest barbs of mental and physical discomfort.

Beyond the parched open field, lined with ragged coolibahs and paperbarks, where the sulphur-crested cockatoos clustered and screeched, shimmered the vast empty plains, the Timeless land, dying off in a dazzle of ochres and burnt umbers, scorched, near delirious under the invincible, all-possessing sun. It filled her whole field of vision, making her eyes glitter. Denied the divine blessing of rain, it was a scentless, soundless, arid terrain. The bird life was prolific, but none of them sang. Drought held the country in thrall, armed with its terrible sword.

Pitiless! Pitiless! Paige turned away, brushing a shaking hand over her hair, pinned close to her small head in a vain attempt at coolness. The hot wind seemed to revel in the misery it was causing. She sighed deeply, rebelling physically and psychologically to an environment that was utterly alien to her. Born and bred as she was in tropical luxuriance, this harsh, eerie land, this ancient, barren land with its vastness and strangeness, was inducing a pent-up emotional state in her. The penalty? ... little trip hammers that staggered her temples, a slight tremor in her pale, slender fingers.

It was a primitive thing that was catching hold of her; a kind of debil-debil thing, akin to the type of psychic terror wielded by the medicine man, the *mul-karee*, black magic. She forced herself to smile at the tension that was mounting in her fine and taut. She'd always been imaginative, acutely sensitive to atmosphere. It would be better when Joel arrived. He was due in at any moment. She tilted her head, her eyes scanning the desolate horizon. All she could see was an eagle hawk coasting in search of prey, a scavenger on the look-out for weakened carrion.

A cockatoo gave an agonized screech of utter abandon and she started visibly, a manifestation of emotional imbalance. God, how unnerving! She shut her eyes, fighting for her customary composure, seeing behind her fluttering lids the mirage dancing bright, the *mari eula*, the dust devils. The satisfactory solution would be to turn about and go home. She was out of place in this sacred land, steeped in legend, the haunt of the Dreamtime gods and demi-gods, good and evil spirits who rose from the featureless plains to roam the countryside performing ritual ceremonies. Yet bizarre as it was, the Interior exerted a queer kind of magic, potentially dangerous. Silvery lakes, unbearably cool and inviting, shimmered in the super-heated air and she had a sudden piercing vision of the beaches back home, blindingly beautiful, crystal clear water, pure white sand. What would she not give for the salt spray caress now? This country around her looked as if it could go up at a touch, in a Wagnerian holocaust. She shivered in the intense heat and looked towards the sky, waiting ... watching, fascinated in spite of herself by the eerie blaze of the sun through the dust haze. For the first time she had in inkling of what the early settlers must have experienced, the shattering fear of the unknown. They too had no knowledge of the vast, windswept Interior; immigrants from the misty British Isles, with their visions of order, county squires and a sturdy yeomanry; pioneers who set out with their absurd caravanserais of sheep and cattle and a few goats to form the spearhead of settlement, lured on by the land fever that still raged in men's blood. Somehow they had left their spirit to hover over the Outback, earned by their crown of courage and suffering, the privations they endured.

Paige rested her aching head in her hands, feeling totally inadequate in the light of adventures that read like the wildest fiction. This was the hard land, the Land of the Lying Light, ruled by an unrelenting and unremitting sun. It had never been conquered, but the overlanders had won a livelihood from it, converted overnight from their separate identities to the uniform 'colonial', a unique Australian type. They must have been strong, brave people and they must have been proud to think they could beat all *this*! This great forbidding wilderness, an unknown fenceless land.

Gradually a vibration impinged upon her ears, growing louder and louder. It was a plane, a twinkling speck in the dust-shrouded blue.

'Joel!' It was a cry straight from the heart. She turned and waved a hand to a tall, spare man in the small office building behind her and he waved back, genuinely pleased to see a smile on the young lady's face. It took no great perception to see the heat was affecting her, yet she had insisted on going out into it to wait for her plane from the Downs. One thing she didn't know. She wouldn't be leaving here today, not with that dust storm brewing. But he'd leave it to young Benedict to explain that to her. To his mind she was the epitome of a city girl – fragile bones, creamy skin, pretty clothes. It'd be anyone's guess how long she'd stick it in the back of beyond.

Out on the airstrip the very air seemed to be leaping with the urgency of the sound of the approaching light aircraft. It all seemed to harmonize with her heartbeats, Paige thought wryly. It was six weeks since she'd seen Joel, though they'd corresponded often. A month since she'd received a charming and friendly letter from his mother inviting her out to Koombala.

The eagle hawk suddenly shrieked and swooped and stuck like some dreadful arrow, inexpressibly savage, then bore aloft a large, grotesquely wriggling lizard. Paige gasped and took a cologne-saturated handkerchief from her bag and patted it all over her face and throat. It gave her a split second's exquisite pleasure, an oasis in the desert. Her eyes stung from blinking at the brassy sun. She moved over to the paperbarks with their thin pattern of shade that heightened the bareness that surrounded them. She felt possessed of a jerky nervousness that was unlike her. What was there to be nervous about? Joel loved her and wanted her out here with him and she was more than a little in love with him.

Joel, blond and handsome with that strange core of vulnerability. The thought of Joel wasn't making her nervous, so why was she acting so oddly? Once she heard his drawling, laughing voice she would be all right again. The trees began to murmur dryly among themselves, encouraging her in her fantasy state:

'We are the trees! *Yamma cooma*, the Great Earth Mother made us!'

The small, secret rustlings seemed loud to her, magnified by her heightened awareness, the weight of a peculiar tension. Perhaps she was a little sun-struck? She stared up at the sky, her narrowed eyes glowing smoky hyacinth. If the rest of Joel's family was like him, she had no need of all the multiple small doubts that buzzed like bees inside her head. Even if they didn't like her, they would keep the fact concealed beneath a blanket of courtesy, if only for Joel's sake. Slowly she realized there was some aching emptiness inside of her unrealized, unguessed-at, until now.

Two days ago, at a 'farewell' office party, she had felt as high as a kite, the object of much teasing envy, excited at the prospect of seeing the legendary Heartland on no less a great holding than Koombala, Benedict Downs. Now, a few hundred miles from her destination, she was way, way *down*! There had to be some logical explanation for it. What would Big Brother Ty think of her? She was stalked by the faceless head of that unknown man. It was fairly obvious that his approval would be essential to Joel, more so, in the purely material sense, than that of Joel's mother. The subtlety of the unconscious mind! Sooner or later it hammered its points home. From her letter, Paige knew Sonia Benedict would be a warm-hearted and charming woman. At a guess, her daughter Diane would be a feminine version of Joel, but the stepbrother, Tyrone, was the unknown factor. She had a quick vision of a steel-jawed, grim-faced individual, with a long mouth compressed from the strain of too many responsibilities, a man of immense self-discipline. Beside such a man she would inevitably appear as gauzy and erratic as a humming bird.

The secret was out, live and unreasonable! She was afraid of Ty Benedict. Afraid and apprehensive. In her mind he loomed more formidable by the minute, as terrifying in his fashion as this pitiless land with which he was so closely identified. With a quick, wordless prayer she watched the light aircraft bank, then approach the long, dusty strip. Cream with bronze stripes, it came down smoothly in the windless heat to make a perfect touchdown a few hundred yards off. The engines cut and the door was thrust open by a long brown arm.

Relief, swift and palpitating, washed over her. She moved, a bright rushing shape, hair glinting, thin, shadow-striped skirt whipping about her, her heart thudding at the sight of a tall, lithe figure moving through a lake of mirage.

'Joel! where on earth have you landed me?' She hurled herself at him and grasped his arms, a funny, catchy little note to her voice.

'Quite obviously . . . the *wrong* place!'

That cool, controlled tone had a ludicrous effect. She stiffened into rigidity and her hands fell away as if sizzled. She stared upwards at a stranger, her face tilted below his, her eyes darkening, her cheeks burning hot. She felt jolted to a stop, out of control, trying frantically to change direction.

He was studying her rather intently with a certain cynicism and a considerable degree of sophistication, thoroughly aware of the difficulty she was having just trying to pull her disordered wits together. His voice was crisp and vibrant with a fine cutting edge.

'Sorry to disappoint you, Miss Norton. You look as bleak as a lost bird. *Ty* Benedict at your service.'

He bowed slightly, his tone mild enough, lightly spiked with irony, but it made Paige come alive. She moved away from him with real grace, smoothly, confidently.

'I'm sorry,' she shrugged, her voice changing subtly. 'It was foolish of me to imagine you'd be like ... *Joel*!'

He looked down at her sharply, a long way. 'Yes, wasn't it?' His eyes were a clear, translucent green, as cool and unexpected as a rock pool.

'You're not in the least like him,' she repeated, tapping her preference home with a silken hammer, deriving a queer kind of pleasure from what was really childish bravado.

But it was true! He wasn't in the least like Joel, but a man of a different species, as strikingly dark as Joel was fair. She might have realized Joel didn't move with that dreadful *sureness*, neither was he so powerfully built. There wasn't a trace of Joel in that male, enigmatic face, so diabolically self-assured. He might have been thirty-four or five, but he wore an air of authority far beyond *that* meagre life span, she thought rather waspishly, reacting to an instant and instinctive sex antagonism. She had read about such things but never really believed in it.

She tilted her glossy red-bronze head to look up at him, her hair curving away from her cheeks, smooth and lucent. 'Let me get my position straight,' she said gently. 'Where exactly *is* Joel?'

The chiselled mouth relaxed a little, amused by her tone. 'I was coming to that. He's laid up.'

She drew in a lungful of scorched air and exhaled it quickly. 'Joel?' her eyes flew to his, anxious, surprised.

'I hope it's not serious?'

'I shouldn't think so!' The green eyes seemed to dance, or it might have been a trick of the light. 'A steer stood on his foot. He'll be out of action for a few days at the most. Needless to say he's deeply disappointed and mortified at such an inconvenient contretemps.'

She turned a vivid face to him, with a hair-trigger reaction flying to the defence of the missing Joel.

'You appear to find it amusing, Mr. Benedict?'

He gave a short laugh, his smile a flash of white out of the darkness. 'You wrong me, ma'am. But one has to be at least one step ahead of the steer. But don't simmer here. Let's go inside.' He glanced at her side-long, his black brows flaring. 'Feeling the heat?'

She was creamy pale, her skin porcelain smooth, her forehead faintly beaded with perspiration, the dusky apricot of sun spots high up on her cheekbones, curved hollows beneath. She should have been mollified, but in fact the terse question, the swift lick of green flame put her shoulders back, provoked the illogical d￼ ￼ be sarcastic.

'Masterly guesswork, Mr. Benedict!'

'And we'll leave it there, shall we, *Miss Norton?*' He took her arm rather tightly, though she tried to elude his grasp. There was a soft set to her mouth and she looked away from him, disconcerted to discover electric sparks crackling faintly on the smooth-skin of her arm.

'Nervy too,' he chided, feeling the tremor run through her. 'I've had a similar reaction from a run-away filly and survived.'

She flushed a little and considered pulling away, but rapidly decided it would be a waste of time as well as

31

making her appear even more ridiculous. She had to content herself with injecting a little false humour into her voice:

'Not at all, Mr. Benedict. You just startled me, that's all!'

He gave a grimace, very faintly malicious. 'I nearly had a coronary myself. Idiotic, isn't it?'

Paige didn't answer. She couldn't, inwardly seething, outwardly cool. She felt troubled, over-stimulated, racing in top gear. Her eyes outlined the shape of his head and shoulders, seeking in vain the gentler contours of Joel. He turned on her suddenly and she started, embarrassed and angry at being caught staring, all the time conscious of a treacherous lack of solidarity under her feet, the quicksand of clashing personalities. It sometimes happened like that, and there wasn't a thing she could do about it. But she *had* to be polite to this man. A great deal depended on it. One thing was becoming fairly obvious, he wasn't going to make it easy for her. But two could play at that game; blind man's bluff. Or reach out and you vanish!

A flicker of amusement crossed his face at her deeply absorbed expression, a personal debate.

'Well, are you coming or not? I can see you weighing up all the pros and cons very fastidiously.'

She swallowed quickly, her throat rippling, confusion fusing in a knot. 'We're not taking off immediately, then? I rather expected it. I've all my things in the office.'

He halted and looked down his straight nose at her without inclining his head, a trick that fascinated her and was vaguely reminiscent of Joel.

'My dear child!' he drawled deliberately. 'Even to aid the lovelorn, I'm not prepared to take off in a dust storm.'

She stared up at him frowning, as taut as a violin string. 'A *dust storm*? But not here?' her eyes began to sparkle indignantly as though he were having a joke at her expense.

'Yes, *here*!' he mocked her with amused impatience, setting her teeth on edge. 'And not too far off. Surely you've noticed the electricity in the air?'

She didn't dare answer that one. The implications were clear, the sarcastic tinge in those green eyes. She had her work cut out not to hit him; box his ears until his teeth rattled. What a pleasure! She tossed her head a little with the dismal thought that she was turning primitive, reacting to the bizarre and savage beauty of her environment. Her heart was beating boisterously with the terrible beginnings of consciousness. Ty Benedict's brand of frank maleness was exasperating; his air of smooth arrogance, so much a part of his physical being, utterly maddening. He was a throwback to the age when men were men and women were just nothing at all! Paige was nothing if not spoilt by the deference and admiration of the young men of her set, but she scarcely realized that. She returned that luminous male scrutiny with one of equal deliberateness.

'I'll brush out my hair next time,' she said sleekly.

'Next time?' His eyes glinted, darkening mysteriously.

'Next time we meet,' she pointed out sweetly.

'How fascinating. Go on. You intrigue me!' He spoke with a deep cynicism and a spark of pure devilry. *And* it was there for all his sardonic, self-contained manner; the inbred streak of the daredevil, a legacy from his father, 'Duke' Benedict, and just let him try to deny it!

She glanced away abruptly as if instinct warned her what thoughts occupied her mind. 'I can see you've a low level of female tolerance, Mr. Benedict.'

He inclined his head, the green eyes lightening and brightening. '*Ty*, please, and stop there, little one. We seem to be going round in circles. Besides, you're working yourself up to the point of a fight. What's up? Can't you take a joke?'

She felt a sudden rush of heat to her cheeks. 'I've never been accused of *that* before.'

'No?' he mused. 'Well, you don't seem to be able to take this one.' His mouth was touched with cool reasonableness. She didn't look at his eyes. She threw back her head and he saw the pale cream of her throat.

'This is different,' she stressed, and fell silent, unwilling to become further involved. He would be a hard man to defeat – this stranger! This cattle baron, with his alert male face, green eyes and eyelashes any female might envy.

A slight grimness hardened his shapely mouth. 'How different?' he pursued the point, not allowing her the easy way out.

'I don't know ... *yet*!' she was stung into replying.

He twisted away and made a half-hearted swipe at a flying insect. 'No, I don't suppose you do. I'm sorry I broached the subject.' His profile seemed faintly bored. He gestured to a jeep parked in the scant shade of the office building.

'You might as well get in the jeep. I'll collect your gear and have a word with Tom.'

The words went in and out of her brain, but they didn't seem to make much sense. He swung away, very supple, very rhythmic, taking her absolute compliance for granted. She stood there motionless, to all appearances refusing the command, the unforgivable thing!

He turned back casually, unhurriedly, as if nothing was amiss, but little pinpoints of light had gathered in the depths of his eyes.

'Go on. Get in. It's not a bit of use arguing. We'll have to go back into town. Another few hours aren't going to make all that much difference.'

She was aware of his downward glance, its rakish quality. She looked away carefully, feeling reality slipping right out of her hands.

'I'll try to remember,' she murmured with some of his own irony. Without being conscious of it her attitude had changed. Her hands fluttered helplessly to her sides, and her bright head drooped. He narrowed his eyes against the searing glare, then moved towards her, took her arm with one of his dominating gestures and urged her towards the jeep.

'You know, I wouldn't have believed it possible to learn so much about a woman in such a short time. You shiver when you're nervous. You're shivering now. And in this heat!'

A long moment passed before Paige regained sufficient assurance to look up at him.

'You're the Boss all right!' she said shakily. 'I can see that right off. I'll do exactly as you say.'

He gave a hard laugh. 'So be it, and I could do

without the wisecracks.'

'Why can't *you* take a joke, Mr. Benedict?' It was out before she could control it, an instinctive retaliatory impulse.

He whistled through his teeth and looked down at her with a glance so careless, so deliberately mocking that the blood beat in her cheeks and her heart fluttered.

'I warn you, lotus eyes, I won't let anything *you* say bother me.'

'That's the right attitude to take.' She forced herself to look up at him, holding his gaze and coming off a definite second best. A pain in her chest seemed to be choking her.

He studied her dryly. 'You know, Joel warned me about you. Red hair and a terrible temper!'

'He didn't. I don't believe it!' She jerked to a stop, wondering why her voice should sound so shaky and bewildered.

'What would you believe, I wonder?' he taunted her, his eyes narrowing, a pure green in his dark, sardonic face. 'Sweet and lovely as wild honey . . . a budding tea rose?'

She flushed and cut him off none too politely for a would-be guest:

'But no one warned me about *you*, Mr. Benedict.' Her manner was an unconscious mixture of provocation, challenge and a definite feline hostility. 'I somehow imagined a regal but friendly reserve. Nothing like *this*!'

He took it well staring back at her as though her particular combination of outline, feature and colour baffled and intrigued him.

'Feeling better now?' he inquired smoothly.

'Very much so!' She flashed him a triumphant look. 'Now that I've passed the initiation!'

He compelled her towards the jeep, handed her in and leaned carelessly on the wheel.

'Who said anything about passing?'

She coloured and let her eyes roam away from him, only to return to settle on his dark face, feeling in a dangerous state of euphoria where the rights and wrongs of things didn't seem important. He was looking straight at her, his dark eyebrows raised quizzically.

'Oh, come now, Mr. Benedict,' she shrugged rather helplessly, 'can't we be friends? Though you must admit you're awfully difficult to be nice to.'

He straightened and laughed, his eyes raking her.

'I've a distinct feeling that would be working on the edge of the impossible. Circumstances being what they are!'

A gossamer tension had spun a web between them. Her teeth clicked in pure irritation. 'My God! you're a brute, aren't you?' she forced the words out, abandoning all pretence at making an ally of this maddening man. Impressions are illusory things, but she had the certain feeling Ty Benedict was trouble!

He watched the bright colour flame in her creamy petalled skin.

'That calls for a little reflection! Let's say I *try*, little one. It's all a man can do.'

'You do try, then. I thought it was natural!' Her soft mouth was set tight, her eyes sun-dazzled. She was rapidly losing control of her tongue.

He gave a slight, devastating shrug. 'Before you start out on something, honey, be sure you know how to get back! Now think that one over while I go get your gear. Cheer up, life's not as gloomy as all that. Not for a girl in love!'

Paige watched him walk away with long, easy paces, nibbling rather savagely on her bottom lip. She was filled with a growing disquiet, but at a loss to know how to correct the situation. Where was her grim-faced individual now? She couldn't have been further from the truth. She tried to fix her attention on the rearing, spinning columns of dust, the weird quicksilver effects of the mirage, but all she could think of was the dangers and difficulties ahead. The wisest possible course would be to keep right out of Ty Benedict's way. It shouldn't be difficult with a man who stood inevitably ... *alone*!

He was back within a few minutes, loading her two bags into the back of the jeep.

'All set?' He gave her a tolerant smile that tautened his high cheekbones.

'As much as I'll ever be!' Her mouth faintly quivered, a dusky pomegranate. 'A stiff drink might go down rather nicely at this stage.'

'Sounds promising!' He turned on her with a vital, swinging movement. 'Tell me, russet head, do you start out as you mean to go on? – because I for one can't guarantee how we'll finish up.'

Startled, she met the provoking glint in his eyes, a speculative, male look, that travelled over her face and shoulders.

'Well, if it helps at all, I find I dislike you less than I did!'

'Well, there's been that much improvement at any rate!'

She moved over quickly, breathless, a little unnerved, as he swung into the driver's seat and switched on the ignition, still looking at her. 'The constraint in the atmosphere hasn't entirely passed me by, Miss Norton.'

'Paige, please!' she said with sweet mockery, trying to keep her face level.

His mouth compressed in acknowledgment, but he made no sound. The engine flared into life and he reversed out and on to the dusty, brown track, waving a careless hand to Tom Blakely while Paige smiled. For a mile or two it was harsh going and eerie in the extreme. Paigne had the queerest sensation of being *watched*. Watched in a vast, empty plain. Baffled, she put it down to the primeval quality of the land, the oldest part of the earth's crust. The dust clouds were thickening now, rolling across the sky hovering ominously, claustrophobically, above them, so low she felt she could almost touch them.

He drove in silence for a while, then glanced at her swiftly. 'Everything all right?'

'Yes, of course,' she gave him a quick, jittery smile. 'Why shouldn't it be? Right up close to the seat of power.'

His eyes met hers briefly, a dangerous gleam in their crystal clear depths. 'It's not as simple as that, flower face. One has to work like a dog.'

'Surely it's worth it?'

'*I* think so!' he murmured dryly, slanting his black brows at her.

She was silent a moment, her face contemplative,

quietly considering. 'Yes, it's *your* country, not mine,' she answered quite seriously, making him look at her searchingly.

'Come now, what is yours?'

'I don't know. I need reassuring.' She turned a transparently bewildered face to him, which appeared to amuse him.

'Very possibly, little one. You're like the rainbow bird, a brilliant if erratic little charmer. It usually turns up about spring, but it's gone by late summer!' His dark face was too bland to be readable, but his voice was definitely sardonic.

Her sharp interrogative look brought forth a brief laugh but no further comment.

'Should that mean something, Mr. Benedict?' she asked suspiciously.

He grinned and didn't answer, but began to whistle softly under his breath. It took a few moments for the tune to impinge on her brain, the words to space themselves out in her mind: 'Every time I see the bright lights, I think of you, girl!'

His mouth was tinged with mockery, her look of comprehension unmistakable, vaguely outraged.

'Don't blame me if you look out of place. This just isn't your natural habitat. How could it be? A slip of a party girl! No, don't interrupt. This is the sombre land, honey, moody, unpredictable, harsh, barren one day, the next, an infinite vista of wild flowers; the air heavy with the scent of boronia, the desert flats carpeted with parakeelya and moola-moola, the white and gold glory of the everlastings. When you live with it it becomes narcotic. At any rate, it's got me. This is *my* country, Paige Norton, our little visitor from the tropics, the

Channel Country, the Land of the Rainbow Gold. A man's country!'

'With which fiendishly arrogant words he silenced me!'

'Exactly! But don't let it bother you!'

She didn't, but she couldn't dispel the upheaval in her veins. In front of them waves of red dust were constantly swirling and always the mirage, beckoning, a thin silver ribbon. Paige rested her back against the hard seat, feeling herself caught up by a furious whirlwind. Her pale hands were folded rather tensely in her lap and she fell silent, too profoundly disturbed to say more.

After a minute he tilted his dark profile to the threatening sky, teak tanned, a shade . . . *ruthless*?

'Sit tight, little one,' he ordered bluntly. 'I want to beat this in. Right now I don't think you could take much more.'

So he was aware of her tension? For a man's man he knew much too much about women! The jeep hurtled along the track that ran parallel to the dry river channels and on towards the town. The changing colour of the sky was quite frightening to her, but it didn't bother *him*, she thought with a mixture of complaint and envy. He drove as he would do most everything else, with a minimum of effort and maximum results; a certain innate elegance and economy of movement that was faintly tantalizing.

The needle swung still further to the right and Paige sat in a shocked silence – she, who regarded sixty-five miles an hour on the open road as the absolute limit! She clenched the side of the seat, almost wincing.

The brilliant gaze met hers fractionally. 'Frightened?'

'Too proud to be frightened!' her voice floated across
to him with feigned insouciance.

His teeth gleamed very white and he nodded his
midnight dark head. 'That's what I like! A girl with an
ever-ready touch of bravado!'

Her nervousness gave way to a half smile that tilted
her mouth. 'A lady usually pretends not to notice when
her word has been doubted, Mr. Benedict.'

'Well, I couldn't be expected to know *that*. Now
could I?' He looked over at her with a curious little
light flickering in his eyes.

She stared back at him with a decidedly puzzled
frown. 'I'm not with you at all. I don't suppose you'd
condescend to explain yourself to me?'

'Sorry, russet-head, that's *classified* information.' He
was staring straight ahead, not moving a muscle, his
head at an imperious angle.

She sighed aloud only wishing you could master the
knack of bettering this man. 'Well, what about your
work, then?' she said with a nice show of interest. 'Tell
me, what do you *do* on Koombala?'

'Whatever for?' He glanced at her earnest young
face, his eyes half closed, a shimmery green against the
dark copper skin.

She was quite rightly incensed by his attitude, the
faintly patronizing banter.

'Silly me,' she said shortly. 'I thought the best way to
please a man was to ask him about his work!'

'You're crazy and you know it!' His low vibrant
laugh angered and disturbed her. She subsided with
comic abruptness and withdrew into a lofty silence,

recognizing once and for all that she stood absolutely no chance of observing the ordinary conventions. Her eyes were stinging, her back aching, her palm *itching*! It was back again in force, the barbaric desire to hit him and draw blood. Something quite alien had entered into her bloodstream. She only hoped it would pass, this tumult of uncivilized reactions. It was quite foreign to her, destroying her carefully cultivated image of cool composure. As a youngster she had been very volatile – the colour of her hair, she supposed, but she thought she had triumphed over that aspect of her nature. She made herself small in the seat, uncomfortably aware of the mocking devil beside her, his lean, powerful frame, the relaxed nonchalance that made her feel inconsequential.

A shaft of incredibly bright sunshine pierced the billowing dust haze and lit up the track ahead for half a mile. There was a peculiar uneasiness in the atmosphere that she put down to the unnatural weather conditions, little realizing that for her this was an end and a beginning. In coming out to Koombala she had set into motion forces over which she would have no control, but at that moment only the thought of Joel was important; Joel! a sheet anchor to cling to. She remembered with gratitude his easy, amicable ways, his desire to please her. Soon they would be together and she would be her old self again.

Only once did Ty Benedict turn to flick a glance at his passenger; the haughty young profile, with its cameo outline. His mouth was unsmiling, but a green fire danced in the depths of his eyes. So this was Joel's rainbow bird? A temperamental young creature, high strung and capricious but with a look of good breeding.

43

He wasn't at all sure Joel would know how to handle her. It would be interesting to see them together. But for himself! ... Paige Norton would have to remain ... *a stranger*!

CHAPTER THREE

Two hours later the dust storm hit the town; a searing, stinging, sinister presence, that kept people furtively indoors, behind locked shutters . . . to quietly suffocate in the blistering heat. It quivered and pulsed in the small hotel room and outside the window the *wee-neera,* the courier of the storm, screeched and beat on the glass with a determined hand, cloaked in a great swirl of red dust. There wasn't the slightest doubt in Paige's mind that a hostile spirit was abroad.

'Damn! damn! a thousand miserable damns!' she whispered, interspersed with a few choking coughs. She was panting and perspiring as she tried not to cry with the sheer hell of it all. It was as bad as being left alone, defenceless, on the outskirts of Hades. How uncertain life was, she thought miserably. To come out here on a high wave of excitement, and now . . . *this!*

To keep her sense of proportion, she began to circle the room, brushing out her hair with short, vigorous strokes until it crackled and leapt like a mad thing. After two very mild gin and tonics, she felt fey instead of reinvigorated. One needed the stiff upper lip in these outposts of civilization, and she was wilting. She came to a halt in front of a dismally spotted mirror, staring disconsolately at her drooping reflection. At least a shower and shampoo had got rid of the finely ground dust from her smarting eyes and nose, inside her small ears, and the roots of her burnished hair. A low-hung lamp showed up the subtle richness of the reds in her hair, but with her pale face, her slender body sheafed in a honey lace slip, she looked as if she was incapable of surmounting any of the advanced rigours of the Back Country.

The fan was oscillating at full tilt, but the air was moistureless, dehydrating; a cold drink, a priceless treasure! It was borne home to her forcibly, convincingly, impossible to ignore . . . she was out of place in this harsh land, as incongruous as a lily on a claypan. In fact, it wasn't beyond the realms of possibility that she could go stark, raving mad if exposed to it long enough.

For a moment her tender young image was overlaid with a vision all blistered and blackened. She blinked and grimaced at her lurid imaginings, attributing them to the sorcery of the storm. Outside in the wild night, the Dreamtime figures walked abroad, full of witchcraft and savagery. She drew a deep breath, trying to revive her customary self-possession.

Ten minutes later she was dressed and lightly made up, looking for all her multiple small miseries as delicate and colourful as . . . what was it Ty Benedict had called her? . . . a *rainbow bird*. It gave her fresh heart. One needed a little camouflage to cope with anxieties, present a brave front to the world. There wasn't the slightest need for Mr Tyrone Benedict to know how she felt: lonely and wretched, transplanted unsuccessfully. But there was something impressive in *his* superb disregard of the vagaries of nature; thunder, fire, storm, the unexpected dilemma of a myriad unseen insects that loved a human target. Nothing could get to Ty Benedict. Not even a woman, it seemed.

She leaned nearer the mirror to check her appearance. Her eyes looked as large as a waif's, the colour of the iris intensified, her skin flawless, faintly shimmery with the lightest possible foundation. She touched her ears and her wrists and her throat with an expensive cologne, smiling faintly to herself at some little thought. Her sleeky jersey was deliciously cool, sleeveless, V-necked, flared from the hip in a swirling abstract pattern of aqua, copper and lilac.

The whole of her body was throbbing with heat and a sicky kind of excitement. She tilted her head with its rufous coppery sheen and walked to the fan, deriving a fractional relief from the rising draught of dry air. There was a tap at the door and she called 'Come in!' then turned around slowly, her hand under her hair caressing the nape.

It was Ty Benedict, a frosty pale body shirt making his dark tan almost startling, an indolent grace in every line of him. His eyes smiled a glittery, complicated sort of greeting, at the same time letting them flicker over her face and her dress, the elegant strappy sandals.

'Well, you did warn me!' he drawled at last.

'Of what?' she looked across at him, mystified, resisting the shivery impulse to recheck her appearance in case something was amiss.

He moved towards her with his characteristic lithe tread, flicking a careless finger at the incurving aureole of her hair.

'*This*!' he murmured succinctly. His mouth turned down sardonically. 'Very nice! The dress too, ravishingly pretty ... perfume! ... a man could go mad for less.'

It cost her an effort to break her slight trance. She

47

spun away from him, perturbed by the sheer male radiance he possessed.

'But not *you*, I feel sure!' She spoke with intense deliberation, slowly, softly, almost as if she was trying to insult him. 'At a guess, I'd say you were a man long since immune to feminine wiles.'

He let her be for a moment, then his amusement flowed in. '*That* was a thousand years too slow! And you're wrong, little one, I can hardly help noticing you're a very desirable young woman. But things being what they are, I can hardly break out and say so.'

'But you *have*!'

He glanced around, the light glinting on his glossy, night black hair. 'Good grief, that was a mistake! Strike it from the record. No one can say *I* don't observe protocol!'

She clicked her teeth with the now familiar rush of exasperation. Her head was in a whirl; she needed another drink badly. Her thoughts were strangling her.

'Your temper hasn't improved any!' he pointed out lazily, noting her agitated movements.

Her mouth twitched bitterly as if she sought to dissociate herself from him ... from her surroundings. 'How could it? Wrapped in a dust storm, quietly choking! It's a wonder the devil himself hasn't made it his headquarters.'

The words sounded melodramatic, but in fact they did fit in with the atmosphere. His eyes narrowed over her thoughtfully, then he smiled. 'One could almost feel sorry for him if he did. Though personally I'd have to *see* the gentleman to believe he existed.'

'It figures!' she laughed despite herself, her eyes

lighting with delicate mockery. She let them linger on his tall, rangy frame, thinking he looked every bit as arrogant as that other – mythical? – gentleman. The closeness of him was ... well, frightening. It flowed over her and she was silent, her mind launching out on to endless patterns. She could almost laugh at her fantasies, but if she let out her breath it would shatter like glass. The spirit of the storm seemed to have taken possession of her.

'Well?' he tilted an interrogative eyebrow.

'Do we have dinner downstairs?' she asked quite inanely, knowing full well where the dining-room was.

He looked at her for a few seconds, perhaps thinking Joel had exaggerated her intelligence, then he smiled:

'That's what I'm here for, ma'am. A cheap but nourishing meal might take the edge off all those grievances.'

Her soft mouth trembled. 'I'm a failure, I know!'

'I suppose you *could* say that!' He made no attempt to disagree, but that attractive, raffish grin made her feel less selfish, less shallow, less disagreeable.

'Actually I *am* hungry!' she lied, her voice as sweet and polite as a small girl at a party. If *he* could be nice, so could *she*!

'Oh?' His eyes glittered with laughter, but he didn't say anything to annoy her. He went to the door and held it with a long arm, waiting for her to precede him out of the room. His manner was faintly indolent, but compelling, that sensed antagonism, well in hand.

A half a dozen fans in the dining-room churned up the near stifling air, redistributing it. It was almost empty except for a harassed young woman with two

49

flushed and irritable toddlers, busily hurling drink straws at one another, their mother, and when she dared to come near them, the waitress; and a group of teenage tourists doing their own thing and regretting it. Their expressions brightened considerably when they fell on Ty Benedict and Paige, but he only murmured a brief, friendly, 'Hi!' and steered her towards the least disagreeable spot in the room, where incredibly the air was cool! – the result of a strategically placed bowl of ice-cubes.

He certainly had a very satisfactory technique when it came to the small courtesies. She was seated and soon found herself gratefully sipping a beautifully chilled Cinzano over cracked ice with a slice of lemon. It was her own voice condescending to try a little iced grapefruit maraschino followed by cold breast of chicken with perhaps a mixed green salad and yes, a spoonful of rice pilaf. She couldn't bear to drink beer, she volunteered plaintively, with the awful notion that it might be the speciality of the house. He told her quite firmly but politely that a Barossa dry white had been put on the ice from the moment they arrived.

She subsided with a little sigh, thinking that at times the dominant male came in handy. Her eyes circled the room. Under different conditions with the windows open to the sun or the blazing stars it would have been a very pleasant place, rustic but scrupulously clean. The table tops were well polished with a soft, lustrous veneer, and protected by attractive place mats boldly printed with aboriginal motifs. In the centre of the tables, instead of the traditional flowers which could not have borne the airless heat, there were black, trough-shaped wooden bowls, filled with tart, shiny red apples.

A stream of synthetic cool air played over her nape and wrists. It was pure sensuous bliss. She lifted her silky hair and let it fall, enjoying the illusion of coolness. While Ty Benedict was talking to a slightly mesmerized waitress, she allowed her eyes unguarded play, her sense of humour making her smile. His was a hard, handsome, face, the face of a man who was totally self-reliant, but it had that devilish streak she had observed before. He was very dark, tall, broad-shouldered, lean-hipped, virile. She had never cared for a man so dark, so explicitly masculine. Neither could she remember a time when she wasn't actively hostile to green eyes! In a cat . . . in a man! But she had to admit that they were beautiful eyes, very clear, luminous, thickly lashed.

The waitress departed rather too suddenly for Paige's liking and he looked back at her, catching her off balance. She flushed and foolishly resented getting caught again.

'You must be tired!' She clutched at any old straw at all.

'I'll manage!' he smiled. 'In fact, I'll put up with a great deal for the sake of a woman.'

She gazed back at him, her large eyes shimmeringly intent.

'Why the witching look?' he queried, faintly sarcastic.

Paige blinked rather helplessly, showing her own long eyelashes. 'Sorry! Was I staring?'

'You were!' he mocked her gently. 'But I've had spells cast on me before tonight.'

'Really!' She raised her delicate brows, rapidly inventing. 'Actually I was thinking what a lovely thing it would be to . . .'

'Hit me?' he suggested.

'The thought never entered my head!' she protested, all the more vehemently because it was untrue.

'May it last!' he echoed her tone, his voice lightly ironical. She nodded to him and he turned his dark head to take the wine from the beaming waitress, preferring to deal with it himself. It was chilled to his satisfaction and he poured two glasses, saluting her over the rim.

'To the rainbow bird. May her trip improve!'

'I'll certainly drink to that,' she seconded provokingly, letting him make what he liked of it.

'Just as you like!' he said calmly.

The wine was in brilliant condition, with a slight greenish tinge and a fresh, flowery bouquet. It rolled over her palate and down her throat, leaving a clean after-taste, slightly acid.

'Now what about a heart-to-heart chat?' he suggested suavely, his eyes narrowing.

'Why not? They're in short enough supply,' she mustered up a cool, sophisticated tone that didn't deceive him.

He smiled, his white teeth very straight and even. 'With reservations, I should say that's a fair comment. But I may have to overcome my natural reticence and pry. Joel is, after all, my brother.'

'*Stepbrother*!' she corrected, rather haughtily.

'Stepbrother!' he accepted the correction, his eyes suddenly glittering like viridian glass. 'Joel's distinction, not mine,' he pointed out dryly. 'My own mother drew her last breath as I took my first. You might say I robbed her of life. But our father was the same. I don't go around making these fine gradations in relationship. My family are ... my family. No fine edgings required.'

Something in his tone stabbed her. 'I'm sorry. Forgive me,' she said with quick contrition, feeling his reproach justified. 'I have a quick, thoughtless tongue. Sometimes it gets me into trouble.'

'That I can well believe!' The exact quality of his glance nearly made her jump. 'But you're forgiven, little one, if it matters!'

It was the answer she expected but didn't believe in. He leaned back in his chair. 'I know Joel is inclined to be touchy about certain things. Understandable, perhaps!'

'Wouldn't you have been?' she asked very simply.

'About what?' His face hardened. He looked a very, very formidable man, alert, dangerous. 'Listen, lotus eyes,' he said curtly, 'the Benedict organization is big enough to take care of the needs of a dozen or more sons. There's work right up to your ears and beyond, but the rewards are great. Joel, for one, has never known the need for anything. In fact a lot of people would call him a very indulged young man, to be envied. His mother adores him, denies him nothing. But he's not a dyed-in-the-hide cattleman, to coin a phrase. He likes his share of the bright lights. A pretty face . . . he's imagined himself in love in the past. Like you?' he added for good measure.

'Like me!' She looked back at him rather blankly for a moment, unable to orientate herself, even forgetting the reason for her being in the Outback.

'Come now, flower face,' he gently coaxed her. 'Either you're in love or you're not. There's no need to look so bewildered. That's what you're here for, isn't it?'

'Money can't buy love Mr. Benedict,' she found herself saying quite obscurely, damning the entire Benedict clan.

'A remarkable thing for 1972,' he observed lightly, 'but you haven't answered my question.'

'And I'm not going to, either!' She crossed her long slender legs, toying with her drink. He was looking at her very intently over the rim of his glass, like the butterfly at the end of the pin.

'I don't know exactly what's in your mind, Mr. Benedict, or what you're trying to lead up to, but I would like to assure you of one thing: there's nothing wrong with *my* life. Just as it is. I have perfect health, a good job, a nice apartment, plenty of friends.'

'In short, you're fed up!' His face was inscrutable, closed up: and the half smile – what was that?

She stared back at him, hostile-eyed, unable to relax.

'Finish your drink!' he said smoothly. 'You'll feel better in a moment. The point I'm trying to make is this. Joel is handsome, good company, intelligent, not to mention he comes from one of the wealthiest families in the State. It's proved an irresistible attraction in the past.'

A thrill of cold steel ran through her. She gripped the edge of the table, already beginning a swift, graceful movement up. 'What a horrible thing to say to me!'

'Sit down!' he said, silky soft, but it had the power to bend her knees again. 'Maybe I'm a horrible man, but you've got to admit the quest for security is common to most women. Joel would be a temptation to any girl. Even you, Paige Norton, for all your undeniable assets.

On the face of it you would seem to be mismatched. There's only one thing I'd like to say, and you can work out the rest for yourselves. Don't mistake a safe harbour for the real thing, and don't let Joel steamroller you into anything you don't really want.'

He could see the sharp rise and fall of her slight breasts under the thin jersey dress. 'You couldn't be further from the truth!' she burst out fiercely, vivid colour flowing into her face, lending it a hectic abandonment, narrowing his eyes.

'No?' his smile held a twist of disbelief, a certain amused contempt? 'To oblige you, little one, I'm prepared to believe almost anything. At *this* point. You've a beautiful soul as well as a beautiful face, utterly incapable of materialism.'

He was looking at her in a way calculated to make her blood pressure sore, arrogant dark head thrown up and back, his eyes glinting, filling her with the momentary fear that here was a man stronger and swifter than all the rest. Danger and doubt began to press down on her and there wasn't a thing she could do about it.

Her pale, slender fingers closed about the fragile wine glass, gripping it tighter, her eyes sparkling like amethysts. Immediately he reached out and covered her hand with his own, lean and strong, tinglingly warm. Sure hands, she thought rather wildly. Hands that could calm a frightened animal . . . a woman.

'I'd advise against any sudden moves, russet-head. I'm too well known here. Anywhere else, of course, you could take your chances and to hell with the consequences.'

Her fingers quivered under his, in an agony of futility.

55

'Entrancing, isn't it?' he said softly. 'The prospect seems to appeal to you. But it won't do, Miss Norton. It won't do at all. Now if I take my hand away will you promise to behave, however much it strains the normal pattern?'

Her hand was released and she was left to massage it, feeling it strangely isolated from the rest of her person. 'But you're the one who's attacking me,' she protested, her eyes enormous, almost filling with impotent tears.

He laughed out loud. 'Strong words, Miss Norton. But this is hardly the time for admiration. If it makes you any kindlier disposed towards me, I don't really believe you're a fortune-hunter at all. Just an impulsive young creature, not sure of your own mind.'

'You're detestable, aren't you?' she asked sweetly, keeping her face serene for the benefit of the approaching waitress. To all appearances it was a scene of content.

'Now there's a remark that could lead to almost anything. If I'm detestable, little one, it's only to *you*. You're a provoking little devil. I don't believe I've encountered your like!'

'Ditto!' she said, swiftly possessed by an imp of mischief. He wore his arrogant ways like an infectious cloak, so why shouldn't she catch a little of it?

'You know I can't wait to see Joel!' she announced in heartfelt tones, as though it had come to her in a startling flash – as indeed it had!

'Now there's a happy thing!' he agreed smoothly. 'Let's drink to it before we come to blows. Our dinner is arriving.'

She took her drink and tossed it off recklessly with a

rapid, impulsive gesture, simmering with a kind of vibrancy that invited him to take one step further and see the sparks fly. In the dull golden lighting, with his head down, the light glancing off his high cheekbones, it was impossible to judge his expression accurately. But she fancied she saw his mouth harden. The whole situation was as explosive, as unexpected, as dynamite concealed in a birthday cake!

She was in the middle of a dark, awesome landscape with rearing red sandhills and dry waterholes and the agonized cries of unseen birds. Draughts of searing hot air whipped around her, the *mirri-witti*, the debil-debil cohorts of the weeners, mercilessly taunting her. Across the sky forked the jagged *indigu*, the black lightning that killed. She cowered and covered her eyes. All of a sudden, she couldn't breathe. She was caught in some strange, claustrophobic horror, clouds of red dust descending on her face. In the deep, inky shadows, towering shapes crouched and muttered, the *kooroongoora*, the terrors that took on human form. Very close by, something, a *presence*, was breathing; a sound that put her hair on end. Paige gave a muffled shriek and flung herself violently forward, half in, half out of the bed. Her heart was pounding and her eyes were tightly shut. Her mind recognized the fact that she was withdrawing from a nightmare, but her body refused to take comfort from the fact.

She was hot, breathless, incredibly nervy. She dragged herself up and switched on the light. God, what a night! She couldn't go back to sleep again, not with dreams like that to haunt her. She walked over to the window and tried to look out. No stars tonight!

57

The wind scarcely seemed to have abated. She bowed her face in her hands as she had done in her dream and gave way to her feelings.

Tears of self-pity and sheer exhaustion slid down her cheeks, and even they seemed to have dried up. She went over to the small hand basin and splashed her face with water, patting it dry, making funny little choky noises in her throat. She would be a wreck in the morning, no match at all for Ty Benedict with his remorseless brand of crossfire.

A definite hard tap at the door startled her. Paige looked around at it uncomprehendingly for a moment, then pulled on her ruffled lemon peignoir, shrugging her arms into the short bell sleeves. She was still in a drugged, haunted state, half waking, half dreaming. She grasped the door knob and threw the door open.

Ty Benedict towered in the doorway. Arrogantly, his dark face grim, his luminous eyes shafting like summer lightning, pinning her to a slide. He was fully dressed in narrow jeans, the shirt carelessly buttoned, the collar standing up, giving him a disturbing, rakish appearance. She stood there transfixed, with a little girl rapt expression, then a sudden weakness overtook her and her heart began a muffled drum-roll.

'Yes?' she asked, flushing a little, angry with herself, angrier with him, still a bit apologetic.

He looked at her oddly in the taut silence, then his face changed. 'What's the problem, little one?' he asked tersely. 'This twenty-four-hour day has to stop. The routine gets deadly after a while.'

He moved past her, tall and formidable, into the room, picked up the pillow and threw it back on to the bed. 'Well?' he turned on her, his winged brows slant-ing.

Paige held the lemon batiste ruffles closer to her throat. She wanted to run, to hide, anything but face him.

'I'm sorry!' she faltered. 'I don't seem to . . .'

He cut her off bluntly. 'Oh, come on now, flower face, at this hour in the morning you can afford to be honest. The strangled yelp was bad enough, but these piteous little noises. . . . It's as bad as having a kitten scratching at the door. A man can only stand so much.'

She bit on her trembling bottom lip, unable to look higher than a pearly white button. 'I'm sorry, believe me. I know I'm behaving badly, but I seem to be be-witched. I didn't realize you'd hear me, though!'

He gave a short laugh. 'My dear child, after a boy-hood in the Big Country, I could hear a pin drop, even if these walls weren't paper thin.'

She could feel the tension in him, the lean, dark vitality that was suddenly ominous. 'I'm sorry!' she repeated herself helplessly, her hands fluttering in a graceful, appealing gesture. 'It's the night, the dust, and the heat. The wind, the *weenera*, whatever you call it. It's got me a little crazy. I know. I always have hated wind. It's so unnerving.'

Ty's eyes flickered over her small distraught face and he relaxed in an instant. 'I have to admit it *is* chal-lenging.'

'Oh, stop laughing at me!' she protested, coming to life, a sudden flash in her eyes. 'You're so sure of your-self, your environment – the unconquerable cattle baron. It's maddening! Enough to make me feel the freak of the world instead of a woman. Women are different, you know.' She tilted her bright head back, defying him to deny it.

'They always have been!' he drawled, the green eyes raking her. 'And you would seem to be more different than most.' He walked towards her and quickly lifted her face with his hand, studying her with a certain relaxed insolence. 'In fact, little chicks like you should be safely married off, then kept on a leash!' His voice was bantering, but his eyes were intent.

'I'm not that different,' she said unsteadily, jerking her head away. 'Just a bundle of nerves.'

He continued to study her, taking his time about it. There *was* a fragile quality to her that did not go well with the austerity of the room, its heavy, utilitarian furnishings. She needed polished light-coloured woods, the shimmer of silk and brocade, watercolours glowing from the walls. She looked lost and small and rather frightened ... his mouth hardened ... and infinitely desirable. Her rose-leaf hair was like satin, her eyes wide and drowning from recent tears, the colour of the waterlilies on the Blue Lady Lagoon on Koombala. Joel would have noticed that at once. As a boy it had been one of his favourite hiding places.

His own eyes were very light and piercing, his mouth firm, the chin resolute. 'Come on now, like a good girl, call it a night. You're in a strained, overtired state, that's all.' He walked over to the bed and jerked the crumpled top sheet off, readjusting it deftly. 'Get into bed and stop worrying. Everything will be different in the morning.'

Paige stood there regarding him solemnly. Everything he did seemed so competent. He didn't look in

60

the least tired. Not with that swinging, dark vitality. Incredibly her eyes began to fill with tears again – weak, womanly tears. She turned away swiftly. 'It will be no damned different at all,' she said jerkily.

He didn't look back at her but went on straightening the bed. 'Now what kind of talk is that? Come on, stop talking and get into bed like a good child.'

The cold patronage was infuriating, the dismissive note in his voice. 'Must you make so much of the generation gap?' she asked ridiculously, wanting to hurt him any way at all.

He only laughed. 'Now that was totally unnecessary! You must be all of . . .' his eyes narrowed over her . . . 'thirty?'

She stood in the middle of the room, pressing her tapering fingers over her eyes, not attempting to rise to that outrageous jibe.

'Oh, go away!' she said a little wildly. 'You make me feel as helpless and ineffectual as a gadfly.'

'You're the boss!' he said with mild sarcasm. 'All you have to do is obey me.'

She could feel him coming towards her with that lithe tread.

'There's always the man you just can't tolerate,' she said jerkily. 'The sort of man who makes perfection seem slipshod. That's you, Ty Benedict.'

'Would you care to comment further?' he asked smoothly as he led her back to the bed.

She shrugged off his hard hand. 'It's nothing *personal*, Mr. Benedict, I assure you. Just an objective judgment!'

'Oh, so you *do* object? You are out of sorts tonight,

aren't you?'

He was determined to humour her at any costs, she could see that. And he wasn't a man given to humouring people.

'Oh dear, you're maddening!' She lay down on the bed, her hair glinting rosy amber on the pillow. 'Insufferable ... an arrogant, green-eyed ... fiend!' She produced the word triumphantly.

His breath brushed her cheek. 'You seem to be drifting into the conversational doldrums, so I think I'll say good night. I daren't say morning!'

Some latent desire to appease him provoked her next unconscious remark.

'I'll never redeem myself in your eyes, will I?' She sounded very young, and forlorn, on the verge of tears again.

'Here now, settle down,' he said firmly.

'Settle down?' Her voice rose and she swallowed, trying to lower it. 'Can't you hear that blasted wind? It's utterly terrifying to me. Oh, please go away. I think I might just pine away of sheer cowardice.'

He seemed to make his decision in a split second, as he moved back towards her. Her eyes were tightly shut, but a tear slid under her heavy dark lashes.

'Oh, lord!' he muttered, and sank down on the side of the bed. He pulled her soft body hard into his arms, in his face, inseparably intermixed, an impatient male tenderness and a cool deliberation. She was trapped now, not by fear, but by complex, leaping confusions, her head cradled against his arm, his free hand twining into her bright hair, a movement that shattered her in its slow motion. Then his mouth was on hers, tilting her head backwards until her breath was gone and the room

62

was a kaleidoscope of colour exploding in a shower of excitement. Her heart rocked crazily, striking into his own, a wild singing in her ears. He was kissing her slowly, deeply, and it seemed to go on for a long time so that she lost the power to move, storm waves rising deep within her, threatening to ride her down. A funny, soft little moan started in her throat and came as a sigh into his mouth.

He was in control again, looking down into her still, creamy face, her eyes deepening and darkening to imperial violet, her slender body still trembling with shock, the roar in her ears abating. His dark face swam in front of her blurred vision.

'I must be out of my mind!' he said with wry emphasis. 'That was the very *last* thing on the agenda.' His shapely mouth twisted in a sardonic smile. 'Put it down to temporary insanity. The night of the *weenera*.'

'Is that what it was?' She stared up at him, still lying back against his arm, watching the light glance across his polished cheekbones.

'That's what it better be!' he said crisply. 'You're not the only one who's acting a little out of character.' He moved abruptly, pushing her gently back against the pillow, standing up to look down at her, his eyes green as malachite in a copper mask.

'But *are* you?' she asked slowly. 'Acting out of character?' She turned her satiny, tousled head to look up at him. 'I think you're a strategist – a coolly precise and skilful strategist.'

His smile was hard, faintly enigmatic. 'Is that any way for a would-be sister-in-law to talk?'

The swiftness of her movements, uncontrollable, unpremeditated, surprised even her. She was on her feet, a small fury, her eyes blazing, taking a healthy swipe at his lean, bronzed jaw. He laughed aloud and warded her off with one hand, before she did any damage, pinning her wrists very effectively.

'You really should do something about that temper of yours,' he said helpfully. 'Not that I don't like the way you look! Don't make too much of a minor incident, a summer night's madness.' He tightened his hold on her, still not hurting her, as if she were a defiant but well cared for child. 'Steady, little one,' he said softly, but there was no mistaking him. 'I promise to forget it, if you will. Besides, there's always the chance that it might take your mind off your other troubles.'

Paige sank down on to the side of the bed, flushed and disconsolate, completely unacclimatized.

'Oh, I hate you,' she said softly. '*You* and this vast, unpredictable country of yours!'

Ty's eyes gleamed as he looked down at her slender young figure. His voice was quiet, directed right at her.

'Keep saying it, honey. Never stop, not for an instant. That way you'll be safe. Now try to get some sleep. The wind should have dropped by morning. If you can't count sheep try playing favourites. Joel would seem to be the logical choice.'

'And why not?' She lifted her head quickly at the odd note in his voice. 'If you're thinking of using your influence against me, I might warn you I have a few tricks of my own!'

He seemed amused by the turn of events. 'I believe you, honey,' he laughed. 'You might remember, though, I've never been known to back down from a situation yet!'

'Now that I can well believe!' she said virtuously, tilting her softly cleft chin.

He gave a short laugh, turning to smile at her. 'Don't let your maidenly indignation run away with you, russet-head. Your own performance was rather superb. In fact, not to put too fine a point on it, I'd say I got considerable co-operation.'

Colour swept into her face, making her eyes brilliant.

'Now that's a damned caddish taunt, if ever I heard one!'

'What rot! You women want it all ways, don't you?' The devilish green glint was back in his eyes again.

She looked away carefully, her eyes circling the room. 'Hide your ego, Mr. Benedict, I'm just casting about for something to throw at you.'

He laughed in his throat. 'You wouldn't dare!' He turned his broad back on her with complete nonchalance, then walked to the light switch and flicked it off.

'Good night, lotus eyes,' he said sardonically, and calmly shut the door.

Paige focused blankly for a moment, then she found her way across in the darkness to bolt the door. So far as she was concerned the *weenera* could blow its head off for the rest of the night. She just had to get some sleep. Never in her life had she acted with so little control, and she couldn't entirely blame it on the weather!

CHAPTER FOUR

SHE woke next morning to cool sanity, refreshed, breathing normally, responding to a temperature drop of almost twenty degrees. *Tya Injarbara*, the Sun Woman, shone through the window and a lovely flush of light fell across the bed. The fearful, driving wind of the night before had almost entirely abated. Now save for the breeze and the birds the silence was complete.

Paige stretched her arms above her head and savoured the moment. The lyrical quality of her awakening seemed to temper the atmosphere. It was all physical, all uncaring, splendid with sunlight that enchanted her eyes. Her smoky gaze slipped over the room, still shadowy with sleep, only in the next second to come fully alert as memory came surging back. Her hands flew protectively to her mouth, her gaze intense, turned inwards, secret yet absorbed. The beautiful bubble of morning had dissolved in the sun.

She moved quickly then, sitting up in the bed, grasping its sides, almost as if she were teetering on the brink of some disaster. She knew she could do nothing . . . *nothing* . . . until the crisis between herself and Ty Benedict had been resolved. A brisk tap on the door and a crisp, authoritative voice roused her, making her heart quiver with shock almost like a physical contact.

'Rise and shine, little one. We leave in just under the hour. I'll have a tray sent up.'

Her eyes were glued to the door. She was breathing with difficulty almost as if she expected the door to fly open to reveal Ty Benedict on the threshold, hands on the hips of his six-foot, panther-lean body, Indian dark, with the unyielding look of high polished steel. She took a deep breath, willing herself out of the tension that gripped her. His voice had an authority, a cool, unfaltering belief in its own powers of direction that unloosed in her a treacherous tide of rebellion. But he wasn't there to see it. His footsteps receded along the corridor and Paige jumped to her feet, decisive, with a high-strung excitement, hot colour in her cheeks. The time might conceivably come when she'd catch Ty Benedict out on the wrong foot. She moistened her soft mouth with no more than a slight tremor and in a matter of moments appeared to have regained her customary poise.

She might never have lived through such a night; a night of wind and high drama that had catapulted her into an unlooked-for intimacy that took no account of the normal, the conventional, the familiar pattern of behaviour. Long before she had time to know the man that was Ty Benedict, his arms had enfolded her, his mouth had left its indelible imprint on her own. It was a fantastic situation. Yet where there was Ty Benedict, she had the certain feeling that there would always be a permanent situation. Her face flooded with excitement, an intriguing brush of adventure, a tincture of shame. She could never like the man, but she had the sense to recognize his brand of hard, compulsive charm.

Five minutes later, the breakfast tray arrived; pineapple juice, cereal, bacon and eggs, coffee and toast. To her mild astonishment Paige found herself eating the lot, locked in a thought-crowded silence, waiting with a strange kind of patience for that moment when she would fall beneath the shadow of the man from Benedict Downs. Ty Benedict was an obvious danger, but there was no need for her to act the shocked maiden aunt. She had a sharp mental picture of herself locked in his arms and her eyes lit with a brilliant hostility and every nerve in her slight body tightened.

She hurried through her shower and dressed in flared blue hipsters with a blue, white and violet filamel body shirt. A matching, battle-type jacket completed the outfit, but it was much too hot to wear it, so she folded it back in her bag. She was on the floor trying to do up the strap when Ty Benedict walked in the door left open by the little housemaid. Instantly the atmosphere seemed to recharge with his turbulent, dark vitality.

'Leave that. I'll fix it!' His tone was crisp, straight to the point, no more than civil.

Paige straightened and turned to him her high-spirited face, willing herself not to change colour. Her eyes were deep hyacinth, deceptively limpid, at pains to hide her peculiar sensitivity to the man. Her smile was cool, rather sensuous, driven by the glinty look he trained on her.

'Good morning, Mr. Benedict.'

His eyes lightened and brightened with the gleam of emeralds. 'Quite one of the most gripping greetings I've ever had!'

'Well, you're smiling at any rate,' she said defensively, 'that's more than I actually hoped for!'

His green, green glance slid over her from head to toe and she stammered abruptly: 'And now I suppose I've said too much!'

'What woman doesn't?' His face was alert and interested, as if he was waiting for her to make her next mistake.

She hesitated momentarily, looking very lost and anxious, then lunged into speech, her eyes great pools of shadowed light.

'About last night . . . I wouldn't like you to form the impression . . . the entirely *erroneous* impression. . . .'

He cut her off with one of his imperious gestures a dark, relentless calm on his face. 'Leave it. It's all here in black and white!'

The sharpness of his tone stunned her, the hard, significant fingers that tapped his breast pocket, inviting her to an avalanche of self-recriminations.

She swallowed and grasped the back of a chair, moistening her suddenly dry mouth. 'What chance have I got?' she asked jerkily.

'That's what *I* say!' His voice was quite cold, as clinical and detached as a judge. 'You had it made. Almost.'

She caught her lower lip between small, even teeth, trying to still its trembling, studying him with intense, almost fearful concentration. Suddenly, without warning, his dark, sombre expression broke up. Something in the depths of his eyes flickered and he gave a white, devastating grin.

'Losing your nerve, flower face?'

'I lost that last night!' she stammered shakily, one hand sliding up to her creamy throat.

'No question there,' he agreed dryly.

'Personally I'd like to forget last night. Agreed?'

'Yes, certainly agreed. I've had a surprisingly irritating few days myself. Set your mind at rest, little one. Our mad moment is completely erased from mind. A man soon develops a conveniently poor memory.'

She caught her breath at his bold impudence, coming perilously close to losing her sense of humour. That same flash of devilry was in his eyes again, the lightning transition from icy impassivity to wicked, sarcastic humour.

'Oh, that was a dirty trick to play!' The tremble of dismay was still in her voice.

He smiled at her, a charming, wholly calculating smile. 'It was all of that, but I couldn't resist it. I seem to be taking a dark glory in provoking one small, volatile redhead.'

Paige whirled about and picked up her shoulder bag. 'You really are the most fearful tease ever!' Her voice was husky, tinged with unconscious allure. 'In fact, if I never see you again I would remember you vividly!'

He smiled at some private, dawning thought. 'Now, there's a gesture of candour I can't follow up. Say it again some other day.'

'I'd be glad to,' she said stiffly, defiance back in her voice again.

'You do that, russet-head!' his voice slowed to a drawl as he bent to her bags, his dark head polished like a blackbird's wing, his purpose whole, undistracted, only faint laughter lines at the corners of his mouth betraying his underlying amusement. There was an aura about him that self-sufficient men sometimes attain; a coiled strength, an awareness, a hair-trigger reaction to all kinds of situations. Just looking at him was enough to put her in a soft fret, as if within the radius of his glance her femininity was to be constantly tested and challenged. Her spine prickled and tautened defensively. Could he guess at her thoughts he would only smile contemptuously with that sculptured mouth.

He straightened abruptly with the swiftness of forked lightning, his eyes slipping over her. Her own eyes half closed as if they sought to protect themselves from the flashing green glint of his glance, the hateful suspicion that he was laughing at her, knew every thought that entered her head.

'Why do you look at me like that?' The words surfaced without her volition.

'You ought to be an expert in men's glances!' A quick lick of devilry flamed in his eyes.

'You're a new experience for me, Mr. Benedict,' she said tersely, her peace of mind skirting a treacherous quicksand of clashing personalities.

'I suppose I am at that!' His glance struck her and held it with a cruel, cabuchon gleam. They were standing quite close together, yet she had the strange illusion that the gap between them widened perceptibly. Beneath the surface exchange of voices ran a deep undertow of excitement, a dark glitter of antagonism that made her tremble with dismay. She turned her small head dazedly, shaking her bright hair, but for the length of a second their eyes continued to hold. His were lit by many green flames, such a power of penetration that she had the dismal idea that he could read her very mind.

He leant towards her his dark, high-cheekboned face taut. There was a tremendous communication of tension between them that both seemed powerless to hide.

'It would be a big help if you could manage to forget last night,' he said harshly. 'Look on it as a malicious trick of fate, some crazy *weenera* thing!'

'Please, I wasn't thinking about it,' she protested, her eyes darkening, the pupil invading the iris.

'Don't lie!'

'Why are you so complicated?' she burst out wrathfully, stung by the brutality of his tone. 'I don't understand you at all.'

'You could try!' he suggested, arrogant, imperturbable, with a characteristic 'to hell with you' expression.

Somehow Paige found the strength to move away. 'I'll try, Mr. Benedict,' she said wryly. 'I'll try. Very hard. Despite the obvious difficulties.' Some little thought must have swum into her head, for a faint touch of mischief lit up her face and her eyes began to glow an intense smoky blue. 'Or alternatively I'll keep up a good front.'

His eyes narrowed, luminously intent, filled with a kind of laconic amusement that matched her own. 'Only in front of the family, little one. That's all that's required! Now it's time we were making a move. You're a long way from home in more ways than one!'

She smiled with her mouth only, conscious of being whirled into danger. His voice came to her ears, laden with a kind of mocking insinuation that held her almost enthralled. She could feel him towering over her with that peculiar, mesmeric dark vitality.

'So you can't move . . . or won't!'

She lifted her head to meet his eyes, forcing herself to combat that white flash out of darkness.

'I . . . *can't*!'

'You can and you will!' His brief laugh held the merest suggestion of indulgence. 'The imperative need, my girl, is to get you to Joel. Remember? Much as I'd like to continue this intriguing conversation there are things to be done on the instant.'

As he was speaking he picked up her cases with one easy fluid movement and she turned to flick a final sideways check over her appearance, straightening her shirt collar.

'Blue! Joel's favourite colour,' he observed lazily. 'It does something for you!'

'I'd like to do something for you, Mr. Benedict!' She followed him to the door, her eyes boring a hole between his wide shoulder blades.

He turned to grin over his shoulder. 'Don't chance it, honey. You'd crash!' He looked so hard, so mocking, so reckless, hooking the door shut after them.

'I'm sure I would,' she agreed hardily in a soft, vehement whisper. 'Remorseless would be an appropriate word for you.'

'Couldn't you come up with a better one?' He overtook her easily, his voice deliberately soft but with a fine, slashing quality.

'Give me time!' She made a pretence of briefly examining a dismally dull watercolour, her softly cleft chin tilting.

He glanced at her briefly. 'Time! The one thing we haven't got!'

Paige walked on stolidly, trying not to think of anything at all. A door opened out in front of her and an elderly woman in a dressing gown emerged, gave a faintly embarrassed smile and scuttled off down the passageway. Paige came to a precipitous halt, her head slamming back into Ty Benedict's shoulder, her shining hair spinning out to brush his cheek.

'No, please, don't trouble to move!' The laughter was apparent in his voice, his breath teased her ear, and she jerked herself free as if he possessed some special power to release the she-devil in her.

'Fear lent her wings, as the saying goes!' he taunted her, shrugging his broad shoulders.

'I'm always quick when I'm nervous. I thought you knew?'

'*Are* you nervous?' his glance whipped over her like green fire lingering on the small velvety mole near her mouth as if he had every right to appraise her. 'You are. That's a fascinating little pulse in your throat.'

She surged ahead, tossing her bronze rose head. 'Does nothing escape those cat's eyes, Mr. Benedict?'

'Cheeky little beggar, aren't you?' he asked pleasantly.

'Insubordination on every hand. Unthinkable for a man in your position!'

He shifted a case under his arm and grasped her narrow wrist, shackling it with a light but inflexible grip. 'Would you like me to point out the logical consequence for all this backchat?'

She tried in vain to release her hand until he did so of his own accord. She rubbed it uneasily, talking more to herself than to him. 'I'm sorry, but all my attempts at friendliness seemed doomed to failure. It's no easy task to win your approval, Mr. Benedict.'

'Keep trying,' he said softly. 'It may be better than nothing.'

Paige preceded him down the twisting stairway,

striving to arrive at an even plateau, a cool, composed state that eluded her. Once she arrived at Koombala, she would have to find an escape route from Ty Benedict. It would be absurdly easy to . . . yes, to . . . *hate* him. She snatched at the idea almost aggressively, yet somewhere on the periphery of her mind an element of doubt lingered that she didn't dare analyse. She sighed dramatically, conscious that in fighting Ty Benedict she was pitching a futile battle or, worse still, what might not even be a battle at all. His eyes moved over her as watchful yet relaxed as a cat's. Suddenly all effort seemed purposeless. She'd be agreeable to the man. No more. No less. The only person she cared about was Joel. His stepbrother was a bolt from the blue, a man with whom she would be wise to call an armistice. Her long lashes lifted and she found herself looking directly into a pair of eyes that were no longer indolent but brilliantly sardonic, sparking off the now familiar desire to cross swords with him. Too many people had been manipulated by Ty Benedict, of that she was sure. Despite herself she felt the heat creep under her skin. She was, in a sense, her own worst enemy, a victim of her own active hostility to the man.

His eyes dwelt on the apricot flush that stained her creamy pale skin and an ironic amusement lightened his tone.

'You're very young, very transparent, rainbow bird. Doesn't it strike you as odd you should so easily and effortlessly resent me?'

'Am I making a fuss about nothing, then?' she looked up at him, startled, with her first show of guilt.

'To your credit you have the grace to look ashamed of it!'

'Of course I'm not!' Her voice was edged with impatience, yet she managed to throw him a smile. 'You do get my goat, Mr. Benedict. You really do!'

His smile was very white, amused, faintly cynical, filling her with the illogical desire to keep it there. She slid her glance away from him hurriedly, afraid he might recognize her susceptibility. A man like Ty Benedict could play hell with a woman.

'Didn't anyone teach a young lady like you to be polite?' he asked with cool detachment, reaching out to open a door for her.

She looked back directly into his face. 'Don't you believe me?'

'Not altogether!' His sudden spurt of low laughter filled her with confusion, openly mocking her. He was in no sense a relaxing person, but a compelling, challenging man. His glance slanted downwards, slipped over her face clouded with a young uncertainty, a patent self-doubt.

'It is possible, young Paige, we might just be friends.'

'It's *possible*,' she conceded lightly, 'but I hardly think *probable*, Mr. Benedict.'

His green glance glittered over her face. 'Here we go again, and why not?'

'That's no concern of yours,' she said evasively, nodding with relief at the clerk at the reception desk.

'Very well then, if the question embarrasses you,' he murmured, a gleam of pure malice in his luminous eyes.

They were walking out of the deep shadows of the

veranda into the emblazoned sunlight. It was like being caught in a spotlight, Paige thought, dazed and bedazzled by the white-hot sun. The heat was growing again and a dry desert wind puffed at their heels.

All the way to the airstrip Ty Benedict kept the jeep moving fast, his hands very lean and sure on the wheel. A silence stretched between them almost as if they recognized the inflammatory quality of words. A flight of lorikeets winged in a gorgeous arrowhead before their path and Paige sat very still, watching them, all the time conscious of the tall, dominating man at her side. The desolation of drought still lay over the land, scorched and primitive, but the birds were fantastic, with their plumage of startling beauty winging against the cloudless peacock blue of the sky. Paige looked about her with almost trancelike concentration, hoarding up the vivid dry ochres of the earth and the unbearable brilliance of the canopied sky.

From time to time she flashed a look at Ty Benedict's dark profile, Indian grave. He had, she decided, as good as forgotten her and immediately suffered an unexpected whiplash of pique. She stared out at the flying road miles, lost in a personality study.

'We're here, little one!' His voice startled her – curt, imperious, guaranteed to snatch anyone out of a daydream. 'That's the *second* time, so you can stop all the soul-searching.'

Her preoccupation fell away abruptly and she smoothed a hand over her hair, damp at the temples.

The jeep ground to a halt, red dust spraying out from under the heavy tyres, and he lifted her out, his hands closing over her narrowing waist, as easily, as purposefully, as if she were no more than a child and a

77

burden to any man. The Piper stood out on the strip and Paige walked towards it almost in a dream while Ty Benedict swung back to the small office. Five minutes later they were airborne, winging their way south-west towards the *Kirrenderri*, the heart of the Channel Country, the home of the giant cattle kingdoms, with a landscape unique in the world.

It seemed to Paige as if they were flying right into the very eye of the sun, the whole world lost in its blinding beauty, the attendant silver-blue waves of the mirage. From her first moment of contact with this strange bizarre land Paige had fallen under its indefinable influence, found herself unwillingly attuned to its eerie vibrations. This was the ancient land, a land of great sanctity to an immemorial brown people. Shimmering far away on the horizon was the haunt of the legendary Rainbow Snake; the Simpson desert, the third largest desert in the world. It was to here that the Great Earth Mother, Yammacoona, banished him for his treachery, his evil and cunning, the mischief he made between the tribes. The natives still called it *Maratjoora*, the Great Rainbow Snake, fifty thousand square miles of shifting, burning sands. Paige adjusted her head comfortably and gave herself up to just looking and absorbing. . . .

Ty Benedict turned to speak to her for perhaps the fourth time in just over the hour, interrupting her own private reverie.

'Your eyes have a restless glowing look, young Paige. I'm not at all sure I know what you're thinking.'

She reacted rather slowly, still caught up in a web of her own making. 'I thought I was an open book?'

A smile touched his mouth. 'At times. Not always.

78

The one thing a woman should never change is being changeable. It gives her the natural advantage of being two jumps ahead of the male.'

She raised her fine, dark brows, irregularly pitched, then laughed, full of a high-strung excitement. 'You know all the angles.'

He slanted her a green sideways glance. 'Well, naturally I'm interested in the more advanced feminine stratagems!' His voice was a blend of cynicism and worldly amusement. 'No, don't tilt that delicate, fastidious little nose at me. I find it rather challenging.'

Her head lowered abruptly. 'I'm a challenge to no one!'

For a long moment he looked right into her eyes. 'You ask me to believe *that*! Joel, for one, has you right up on a pedestal.'

She began to smile. 'How dreadful! I've no head at all for heights.'

'Yet you bear no scars!'

'No!'

They were still fencing with each other, recognition made final by the look in his eyes. He was frowning slightly, his clear green eyes deeply concentrated on her. It was like going down in a fast lift, Paige thought distractedly. Perhaps she was, as she had never hitherto suspected, sexually timid, seeking only the conventional in a man. Something about Ty Benedict both excited and frightened her. He was outside conformity, nonentity, frustration, yet communicating a sense of unease that was darkly strong.

A look of deliberation seemed to harden his face, shadowing his strong cheekbones. Seen like that he hadn't, by any stretch of the imagination, a *kind* face.

It was uncompromisingly masculine, well born, with a fiery male pride, visually striking. There was a present, a past, and a future indelibly stamped on him; a difficult, dangerous man whose intense good looks were further enhanced by his expression, the outward manifestation of a cynical adult brain. Just once in a while you might meet a man like that, but then they were too difficult to handle. She stared out the window with a slightly masked expression seeking a change of topic, something safe, something easy, anything to relieve this all-present communication of tension.

'Incredible to think the wind dropped so suddenly,' she managed in an even, conversational voice. 'I'm afraid I didn't cope too well with it.'

'Not so surprising!' he said, equally matter-of-fact. 'The variable winds cause a great deal of irritability and instability out West, especially among the aboriginals. I remember once when I was a boy being lost in the Calidgera country during a dust storm, a sheet of flame across the waterless wastes. Every known landmark was wiped out without trace. Malabuk, our head tracker, found me. He was a high-ranking medicine man for the eagle-hawk tribe, a wonderful old fellow providing you never crossed him and observed all the tribal taboos and sacred places. His wraith was said to have possessed a very potent magic. He was one of the real old-timers. He could cross the roughest, driest part of the Run. He knew all the gnamma holes, the secret waters, the sacred drinking places of the Great Watersnake. And there's his haunt over there just beyond your wing tip. *Maratjoora*! Koombala is right on its fringe. Waterless except for the good seasons when streams enter it from the north-west. Then the claypans turn into lakes alive with great concentrations of birds; pelicans, wild duck, black swans, terns. The sandhills are covered with the *moola moola* and the pink and purple *parakeelya*, the crimson flame of Sturt's desert pea with its staring black eyes. A desert that's no desert,' he said reflectively, 'for millions of seeds lie just beneath the surface ready to germinate at the first drop of moisture.'

He turned to look at her and there was an extra brilliance in his eyes. 'If you look down you'll see we're flying over Three Rivers Country: the Diamantina, Georgina, Cooper. The rivers and their channels flow right down between the sand ridges. In some places you'll notice you can hardly trace a bank, but when the rains come you can guess at the water lying about!'

'Lakes of flood that dissolve into lakes of green grass!' she said dreamily, letting her imagination substitute for her. 'What kind of grass?'

'Saltbush, bluebush, cottonbush, parakeelya, cane grass, vines, creepers, any amount of drought-resistant herbage. It's sweet country, never sour. Great cattle country. We're waiting for the rains now. Maybe you've brought them in with you, *Atnar-kan-now-an-ondra*?'

'Which is?' she turned to smile at him, with a subtle change in her manner.

'The Bird of the Opal Fire. The rainbow bird,' he mocked her. Beyond his dark, handsome profile was a boundless space, a deeply blue infinity on which she could fix her attention. Ty Benedict was dynamite – an indisputable fact. She made the silent admission abstractedly, but she couldn't bring herself to look back at

81

him, not meet the crystal clear glitter of those remarkable eyes.

His mouth firmed with a trace of irony and he straightened, head flung up, rather imperious. He spoke with a crisp intonation and she knew he was aware of her every overture and withdrawal. 'Water is life out here, little one. Rain, a divine benediction. Koombala is luckier than most. We've permanent water and plenty of bores to keep us going even in the worst times. And there it is coming up on the starboard wing. Koombala, Benedict Downs!'

As he spoke a change came over him as indefinable as it was unmistakable. She cast a swift look at his chiselled profile then out over the wing tip at the vast colour canvas that was Koombala. Her eyes glowed with a heady, reckless excitement, colour whipped into her face. For the first time in her life she came close to realizing a man's great passion for possession.

Koombala spread out as far as the eye could see, a great heritage, a million acres of sacred ground, fabulous cattle country. Great towering red sandhills broke in multi-coloured sandstone formation; chains of twenty miles or more pounding across the vast mulga plains with their eerie invocation of the inland sea of pre-history. A maze of water-bearing streams crisscrossed the Big Run, threading a path through the towering sandhills, the main arteries still carrying plenty of water, the smaller channels long since drained dry by the all-powerful sun.

Peace. Silence. The ancient red land. The silver-shot air of the desert had a preternatural clarity, lending to the kiln-baked colours, the dazzle of dry ochres, a bizarre brilliance that beggared description. These were Namotjira colours, faithfully reproduced by the greatest of the aboriginal artists, on canvas, to the uninitiated eye, too vivid to be truly believable, but to Paige, from her wonderful vantage point, the ultimate truth. This was the real Australia, the beating heart of the great island continent. It was all there, just as Namotjira had painted it; the rose-red, the violet, the flame blue and fiery cinnabar. Every natural feature stood forth with a barbaric kind of splendour, harsh, unyielding, a man's country, the Big Country, and she made a funny little sound aloud, her first sight of Koombala forever imprinted on her mind.

Ty glanced sidelong at her passionately intent young profile. 'So the rainbow bird can still respond to the call of the wild?'

Her eyes found his, clung to them compulsively. 'I can't imagine anyone who couldn't respond to all this. It sets you apart. Out of the ordinary. Beyond the everyday conformity. A great heritage. One reason you are what you are, I suppose. I envy you, Ty Benedict!'

'You're quite a surprise packet, Paige Norton,' he retorted, something in his voice drawing her eye, back up to his, coloured with an expression to which she had no key. All she could fathom was that it was new to her.

'Am I?' her voice was husky, the necessity to break away from that unwavering scrutiny, unbearable.

He turned his own head, ablaze with a matchless dark vitality, and she found herself saying:

'I can even go one better. Resurrect some fragment of verse from my schooldays. . . .

"But if you have fought the forces of the
Drought and Dust and Storm;
If you've ever tailed the horses
On a far-out western run;
If you've ever heard them neighing
As they gathered to the whip,
You will understand me saying
I would let a fortune slip." '

His gaze returned with interest to her face, some
little spark flaming in the rock-pool depths of his eyes.
'Will Ogilvie, "Saddle for a Throne",' he said lazily.
'You know, little one, you've got just the right kind of
voice to make a man listen.'

'Oh?'

'Vital, inflected, rather low-pitched.' His glance
swung down and struck hers. 'Joel's lucky!'

'What about me?'

'Oh, you could have been luckier,' he said blandly.
'You could have got me!'

She smiled with genuine amusement. 'All this and
modesty too – a rare combination, Mr . . . Ty?' she
broke off at the look in his eyes, her own eyes lingering
on his dark face touching on each separate feature.

'That's better!' he spared her a narrowing glance.
'Who knows what other surprises you might have in
store for you!'

Her widening eyes flew to his face, the colour intensified, her dark brows arching.

'Don't go wasting the woman magic on me, honey.
I'm a seasoned warrior!'

It was such an obvious fact that she laughed and
earned for herself that white, disarming smile that lit

84

up his face.

'Shall I tell you something, little one? You could, with the right handling, become quite a woman.'

'All I have to do is do what you say!' It was such a spontaneous admission, so thoughtless, so unconsidered that the hectic, wild-rose colour rushed into her face.

'Did I say *that*?' his voice had an odd little inflection in it, his green eyes as malicious as a cat's.

She murmured with a world of self-disgust in her voice:

'Consider that unsaid. You were born to provoke...!'

'You're making that up ... all of it, pretty bird!'

The aircraft suddenly dipped to the right, losing altitude, and she looked down at an incredible sight.

'There are eagles below us. Great wedge-tailed eagles with golden eyes!'

He laughed, and she could see it was at her. 'I know, little one. Now damned well sit still and strap yourself in. You can't beat a redhead for making distractions!'

In the silence she said carefully: 'Well, it shouldn't be for too much longer.'

A flash of amusement crossed his face. 'I haven't the time to assess that little jibe. I take it you don't fancy yourself as mistress of it all.'

'Good grief, no!' Her whole attention was trapped. 'The mind boggles at the extent of the role!'

'Oh, I don't know,' he smiled his disagreement. 'The right woman could take it in her stride. One of these days I'll take a wife. Time's running out, I guess,' he laughed under his breath and flicked her a sidelong glance. 'I suppose a man is entitled to hold out for what he really wants.'

'Yes?' she paused, sour-sweet.

'Don't tell me, I know. You can't understand how a man can be aghast at the thought of spending three hundred and sixty-five days a year with the same woman!'

'A man might just like it,' she said sweetly. 'Wouldn't that be a surprise!'

'It would indeed!' He tossed that off carelessly, sunlight streaming over his arrogant dark head.

'Dare I ask what type of woman would attract you, Mr. Benedict?'

'Who said anything about attract, Miss Norton? I said I need a wife!'

She sighed elaborately and avoided his eyes. 'I might have guessed the cold-blooded approach!'

He gave a great shout of laughter that thoroughly rattled her. 'Now you, Miss Norton, should know the opposite!'

Behind the brilliant green glint in his eyes she could almost see his mind working. She shook her head fretfully, feeling herself pinned out like a butterfly. 'You talk in riddles,' she said aimlessly.

'. . . to confuse little girls.'

Quickly she lowered her heavy dark lashes. 'I'm desperately sorry. You must find me very trying.'

His voice was sharp with a kind of amused impatience: 'Did I say trying? Different, certainly. Last night. . . .'

'I thought we agreed to forget last night!' she almost flung out an imploring hand to him in her confusion.

'Now, now,' he said soothingly, 'a joke's a joke!'

'Not with you around!'

'Quit now, honey, while you're in front. Women get kissed every day.' There was a note of genuine amusement in his voice, that further incensed her, as though he was explaining a very simple fact of life to a child.

'We're coming in to land in a few minutes,' he said conversationally. 'Don't you want to fix your make-up?'

It was an obvious jibe and she responded to it as such. 'Why, does it need it?'

His voice was lazy, but his eyes were anything but. 'You know darn well you have a skin like satin.'

Her head jerked up and she took a quick, deep breath. 'I wasn't fishing for compliments, Mr. Benedict!'

'You'll be fishing for a broken neck, honey, if you don't stop calling me Mr. Benedict! It piques my sense of the ridiculous.'

Something in that brusque statement turned it into a challenge; the set of his head, the downward look down his straight, classic nose. the cabuchon gleam in his eyes. It was hard for her to answer him casually.

'What do you want me to call you?'

'Ty!' he said laconically, his shapely mouth curving. 'That will do for a start!'

Her voice broke in quickly. 'I do believe it suits you. Ty. Tyrone!' Oddly enough the name rolled easily over her tongue with a musical lilt.

'There now, it wasn't such an ordeal, was it?' His eyes withdrew from her face. 'Look down, little one, Joel has made it out to the airstrip. The girls too, unless I'm mistaken. Nervous?'

'Never again!' she said with an involuntary teasing grin.

'That's my girl!'

It was a figure of speech, of course. He certainly didn't mean it. Paige looked out the window and the Piper began its descent, skimming the tree tops like some mythical bird, homing in to the earth, braced for the point of impact. Paige sent her glance winging on ahead.

Seen from the air it was like coming in to a tiny, self-contained township. Set high on a slope overlooking the dense green of a lily lagoon was the Big House, Koombala, a homestead of mansion-like proportions, built in a square U, the first home 'Big John' Benedict had built for his bride. Outside the wide radius of its lush green gardens constantly watered by subterranean bores stood the stockmen's bungalows, one, probably the overseer's, bigger than all the rest. To the right of the homestead were the stables, the saddling rooms, an administration block, a general store, a show ring, countless holding yards, and farthest away from the house, its own private, all-weather air-strip.

'Home!' Ty Bendict said briefly, and Paige was conscious of the latent pride in the words. 'And you never knew you loved Joel so much,' he tacked on mercilessly.

She looked swiftly at him, then away again, her stomach muscles gripping, not only a physical reaction to landing. The Piper flew on straight for the silver glinting air-strip and made a perfect touchdown in the windless heat to run on for a hundred yards before the engines cut.

A little pulse began to visibly hammer away in her temple. She moistened her mouth, soft and sensuous, put her hands to her glistening hair.

'This is it, honey?' he said crisply. 'Primitive adventure in the Australian Outback, or whatever became of the rainbow bird?'

She was aware of the closeness of him, the grip of his hand on her shoulder propelling her out of the small cockpit. 'Now you're here, you don't seem to want to get out!'

'Try me!' she tossed her bright head at him.

His eyes flickered and he gave that white, disarming grin. 'Don't tempt me, honey child!'

The air hit them with a dry, aromatic breath and Paige was spun down, distracted by the over-all pattern of shimmering flatness that ran away to jagged rose-red ranges sharply outlined against the peacock sky. There was a welcoming blast on the horn of a jeep parked some little way off in the shade and a flight of tiny orange-coloured birds rose in myriads from the coolibah trees, screeching their protest. Far away in the distance, sending up cloud castles of red dust, roughly a thousand head of cattle were moving fast, bunched in a solid mass, stockmen circling them round, bellowing and tossing their heads, splitting the silence of the thin, rarified air of the desert.

Paige half closed her eyes against this new, overwhelming landscape, the baffling, beautiful sea of mirage that danced like a live thing over the strip. A small, slender blonde girl detached herself from the group at the jeep.

'Ty!'

She came on at a half run with a neat, clean, young girl look, lightly tanned skin, lovely hair caught back at the nape, a lively, intelligent face, but not a pretty face. So far as looks were concerned the Benedict men seemed to have unfairly grabbed the lot.

89

'Paige! Hello there!' She caught at Paige's hand with a quick, warm gesture. 'I'm Di. Quick off the mark in everything – believe it. Anyway, Joel's all tied up in knots, mortified beyond belief. A bear with a sore head. His foot, you know – Ty told you, of course. The poor boy's grounded, but completely. I'm so glad you're here. You're lovely, really lovely. One never knows whether to lend Joel an ear or not when he raves on!'

Ty Benedict leant a restraining hand on the girl's shoulder, his dark autocratic face surprisingly indulgent.

'Tactful little soul, isn't she? Show a little finesse, Di. I don't imagine Paige wants a whole family run-down in the first five minutes. Lead up to it gently.'

Di gave a small grimace in which there was an element of chagrin.

'Don't let him crush you!' Paige said quickly, returning the younger girl's smile. 'I'm just as interested as I could be!'

'An ally! an ally!' Diane crowed, and Ty Benedict laughed aloud as he watched his stepsister take hold of their visitor's arm in an engaging, wholly friendly fashion. Her clear young mezzo dropped to a near whisper.

'See the snooty raven-haired beauty in the jeep beside Joel? That's our Tracey, Mother's godchild, and a godawful child, but now a very important person. Accept it and you're over the first hurdle.'

'Di!'

Diane's face flushed as she looked up at her stepbrother, then some of her grin came back. 'Oh, come off it, Tyrone, me lad. I'm only trying to put Paige in the picture. Forewarned is forearmed, so they say!'

'That's it, Di!' he said with finality. 'We'll just go along in easy stages. Now it might be an idea if you take Paige over to the others. Joel seems to be having the devil's own job trying to get out of the jeep.'

Di looked over her shoulder, noticing her brother's efforts which made her do no more than chuckle. 'We'd better shove off. Tracey looks very regal, doesn't she, staring straight ahead, precious girl.'

'I'll get the gear,' Ty Benedict said repressively. 'Off you go!'

The two girls moved off on the instant, Paige moving a little ahead, the brilliant sun on her bare head like nothing she had ever felt before.

'Joel!'

He was so busy trying to get out of the jeep he scarcely lifted his head, from the mutinous set of his mouth audibly cursing his disability, fumbling with the door of the jeep, completely unaided by the dark-haired girl at his side. Finally he made it, hopping on one foot to the ground, falling back against the side of the jeep to let it take his weight.

'Red!' There was a trace of physical pain in his voice, a wry set to his mouth. 'Damn and blast! Let the mountain come to Mahomet!'

There he was; lanky, lean Joel, gracefully slouched, his narrow golden-brown face lit up with intensity, the sun glinting on his shining blond head. He extended his long arms and she went into them gratefully, expecting, and wanting to return, an affectionate welcome. She was not prepared for the passion and hunger of his grasp, the kiss that tilted back her head, stretched her neck painfully, crushed her shell pink mouth and brought the blood beating to her face.

'Darling!' He freed her mouth but kept his hands on her gentle, but possessive, the fingers trembling slightly.

'You'll have your work cut out to cap that!' his sister observed with acute interest. 'That's what I call first-rate. Would that someone would kiss *me* like that!'

Joel ignored his sister's comment if he even heard it, his hazel eyes slightly dazed with the force of his emotions, the jagged pain across his instep for once forgotten.

'Paige! You're the most beautiful thing in all the world!' he murmured, his voice buoyant with feeling.

'I must say I admire your social sense!' the dark-haired girl announced very crisply in a light, precise voice that could still stop a crowd.

Diane frowned at him. 'Forget it, Tracey. This is a moment of real contact – profound. I'm even wondering if all the poor boy said was *true*!'

'Oh, never mind!' The dark-haired girl subsided with an unjoyous expression staring ahead to where Ty Benedict was approaching, while Diane continued to look at her, surprised at her face and her tone.

'Ty, welcome home!' The soft, sweetly feminine ejaculation seemed right out of character.

Diane looked at her stepbrother's sleek dark head, her greeny-grey eyes glinting humorously. 'Tracey's patrician nose is slightly out of joint. Joel's still in orbit, unmindful of his manners.'

'Nevertheless she's right!' Ty Benedict said in a smooth, urbane voice, depositing Paige's cases in the back of the jeep. 'Joel, old son, how about making some introductions?'

The tableau broke up abruptly as Joel fired a glance at his stepbrother. 'We were expecting you yesterday!'

'Yes?' One strongly marked brow shot up. Ty found a cigarette in his pocket, took his time lighting it, drew deeply and turned back to the younger man.

'Sundown at the latest,' Joel persisted.

His stepbrother gave a brief laugh. 'I'm good, but not that good! Let's discuss it some other time.'

Joel collected himself with an effort, trying to withdraw behind his own brand of humour.

'It's risky, I know, but here goes. . . .'

Paige let out a faintly stifled breath, the immediate world still slightly out of focus. The warmth and glow of pulsing blood filled her lips and her cheeks, deepened the colour of her eyes. She turned her head to smile at Tracey Ord as Joel introduced them, barely hearing his voice. Somewhere warning signals were flashing on and off. This girl didn't like her – worse, would *never* like her! Her position had been challenged in some inexplicable way and she was dead set on maintaining it. Joel had recovered himself, his manner easy and charming, lightly amused, while Ty stood back a little from the rest, lazily smoking with a look of half affable detachment, his green eyes hooded behind a thin veil of smoke.

Diane kept up a stream of inconsequential nonsense, but Tracey Ord jarred and jarred – the look in her long turquoise eyes, the blunt appraisal, the faint trace of condescension. She was more than ordinarily good-looking. She had beauty. Her eyes were striking, the nose high-bridged, slightly humped, almost aristo-

93

cratic. Her mouth was thinnish but well shaped, her chin very firm. Though her skin was deeply bronzed it had the flawless sheen of perfect health and vitality. She looked older than her early twenties; a tall, strongly slender girl with the damnedest manner Paige had ever yet encountered. Her fixed gaze held to Paige's face, cold as space, sharp enough to be dangerous. Then she smiled, her lips faintly curling. Paige smiled too, but they both knew where they were – inevitable antagonists. Over what?

Diane broke in on the waning conversation: 'Did you ever see such beautiful hair? It's a fabulous colour, Paige. You're awfully lucky to miss out on freckles.'

Paige turned to smile at her, grateful for her uncomplicated approval. She gave her head a light shake that fanned the bright hair into the full light and heat of the sun. A hundred dancing highlights glinted along the silken strands, bringing an involuntary leap of desire into Joel's eyes. It didn't go unnoticed. Only Ty Benedict leant against the jeep surveying the scene with a face entirely neutral.

'Incidentally, we might make it up to the house,' he said easily. 'Sonia will be waiting!'

With a swiftness that suggested sleight of hand he had them organized and piled into the jeep, turning his dark head with a gesture suddenly imperious. 'Move over, Tracey, I'll drive!' He looked over to the back seat where Joel was having small struggles with one of Paige's cases.

'Need any help, Joel?'

Joel shook his blond head with a kind of bridled frustration blazing out of his eyes. 'No, thanks!'

'Too damned obstinate to admit it!' Tracey supplied

94

in a deadly cold voice. Simultaneously Paige caught a deeply green gaze in the rear vision mirror; a gaze that plainly said: 'Well, you're here now, little one. What in hell are you going to do about it?'

She jerked her glance free, feeling a tug on her hand. Joel was looking reproachfully into her face. 'Drat this foot! It's kept me a prisoner. But for it I could have had you all to myself.' A shadow slid over his face. 'Paige, sweetheart, I've been so lonely and bored. Afraid of someone else getting you.'

Di flickered a glance over her brother's 'small boy' rather lost face.

'Come along, sonny, speak up!' she urged him in a monstrous stage whisper. 'I for one don't intend to play gooseberry!'

'And what's that? Some stupid game?' Tracey demanded scornfully from the front seat, giving them the benefit of her aquiline profile. Her eyes struck contemptuously over Paige's small, creamy face, turquoise no longer, but black as slate.

'Mind your own business, Tracey,' Joel said rudely, blinking his long eyelashes as if he were coming out of a dream. He had one of Paige's slender, oval-tipped hands crushed up in his own, then lifted it to his mouth and kissed it. Paige felt the colour come under her skin and Di gave a hoot of laughter.

'We are all on edge today, aren't we? Take no notice at all, Paige. You've created a sensation. Lovely enough to ensnare any man!'

'Do you want to get yourself throttled?' Joel turned abruptly on his sister, his hazel eyes sparking fire.

'You bounder!' She subsided with a muffled giggle, eyeing him doubtfully.

Ty Benedict changed gear and spoke from the front seat with crisp decisiveness. 'The usual thing with graceless adolescents is to let one of them walk home. Which one is it to be?' His tone was cool and measured, the faintest bit bored, but it had the required effect. Beside him Tracey went rigid and Diane sank back speechless, pushing back her hair.

'You might at least be considerate of my busted foot!' Joel complained rather petulantly to Paige's ears, as though the sight of his stepbrother's whipcord virility infuriated him.

Ty merely grinned. 'Don't get yourself all excited, old son. We're only accepting Paige as one of the family . . . or the next best thing.' He sought and found her cameo face in the rear vision mirror and smiled, his shapely mouth moving. 'Don't look so worried, little one. You're going to love us!'

She saw the sparkle in those crystal clear eyes, the lurking devil that made her quick temper surface.

'That's nice to know, Mr. Benedict.'

Joel suddenly caught, then cupped her softly cleft chin in his hand, pressing a kiss into the corner of her mouth as if he could help himself no longer and didn't much care who knew it.

'Oh, Paige honey, for the first time in my life I'm tongue-tied with a girl!'

'Would you please say that again,' her sister begged him irrepressibly. She straightened her slender, twisted body, the corners of her mouth lifting. 'There's only one thing in life worth having, folks, and that's love. L.O.V.E.!'

'And a lot of money in the family!' Ty Benedict capped her neatly, a white smile flashing across his teak-tanned face.

'Love's a delusion,' Tracey Ord announced savagely, in a woman-of-the-world, weary voice. 'It's as simple as that!'

Nothing, it seemed, could clamp hold of Diane's tongue. 'Oh, do let's stop and chat about that. You've got to be terribly intelligent to pass a remark like that!'

'Oh, for God's sake, Ty, can't *you* stop Diane?' Tracey demanded, her soot-black hair winging back.

'Who's ever been able to do that?' he responded rather blandly. 'Once you get used to her you're all right.'

'There's an answer!' Tracey's fine cut mouth drew in.

'Well, this way we might even succeed in getting up to the house.' He threw her a sidelong glance that conveyed an explicit message. His glance swung back to Paige with a gleam of lively malice.

'Welcome to Koombala, little one!'

She stared at the back of his smooth dark head. 'The only question is, will you all like me?' she asked sweetly.

He grinned and she caught the pulse of laughter in his voice.

'We'll relish the chance!'

One either side of her Diane and Joel smiled into her face, the family resemblance suddenly strong, but Paige, with a woman's intuition, read Tracey's mind, the cold condemnation. She looked back at Ty Benedict, his head on his wide, powerful shoulders thrown up and back, his physical presence extraordinarily compelling. An arm slid about her shoulders and Joel murmured into her ear:

'Hey now, switch back to me!' He touched a gentle finger to her cheek. 'Look at me, Paige, please!'

Somewhere in the depths of his hazel eyes she caught a glimpse of a dark, swirling resentment and with a rush of contrition she tried to coax him out of it, covering his hand with her own at the curve of her delicate shoulder, all the while conscious of a voice inside of her shouting and shouting: 'What on earth have you let yourself in for?'

Now at this moment she was no longer certain she was in love with Joel, no longer certain what she was going to say to him. Yet she knew with a little stab of compunction that Joel would find it hard to take no for an answer. All she could do was wait and see what tomorrow would bring!

CHAPTER FIVE

It was the hour of sunset and the giant landscape had shed its glaring hostility. The sky of brass had turned to a sea of gold and over on the western horizon an armada of sailing ships, ancient and pagan, ran before the wind, their sails billowing flame. It was an incredible sight, breathtaking in its colouring and imagery. Birds were calling across the long silences, the wild geese and the brolgas, the sweetly liquid notes of the butcher bird, the whirring flight of topknot pigeons. A brilliant shaft of sunlight shot from heaven to earth, illuminating their path, piercing the massed cloud cover.

Paige pressed her forehead against the big, fixed sheet of glass. She was standing quite still staring out over the garden strip that flanked each wing of the house. It was ablaze with tropical colour, heavy with unfamiliar scents; the exotic kind of plants that grew on the sand flats. It was all so very different! So compelling it filled her with odd little tremblings. This was the land of terror and splendour, with two faces to frighten and confuse the newcomer.

It was still very hot and she slipped a hand under the bright curls on her nape. The desert ridges glowed incandescent on the skyline, fiery, like burning coals, but within the hour, Diane had told her, the endless shimmering plains of mulga and spinifex would cool down, cloaked in the purple-blue shadows of a desert sundown.

Paige experienced a curious little tremor and rubbed her hands over her sensitized arms. She had never before realized the immensity of these great holdings, the fascination that fact alone could exert. Outside her window grew the graceful, massed pink and white and cerise, blossoming bauhinias, and on the edge of her vision, compelling the eye, a stately desert oak, a beautiful tree, with a barrel of thirty feet or more of unsurpassable timber, flanked by the shining spears of the minareechie, the red mulga, with its glossy green foliage, surely one of the prettiest woods of the Outback. At the end of the green strip of lawn great drifts of rose-pink bougainvillea fell over a high fence of white latticework, fringed by a shady grove of poinciana, acacia and casuarina, yapunyah trees with their blossoms gently swaying from the attentions of dozens of greedy little honey-eaters.

She gave a soft mingled sigh of sadness and pleasure; that fine edge of sadness that beauty could bring. Always and forever, wherever she went, she knew she would carry within her the sight and the sound and the scent that was Koombala: an oasis in a vast infinity of wide shallow valleys and blunt-nosed sandhills, dotted with the wonder grass, the spinifex, and the sombre little saltbush with its brothers the cottonbush and the blue bush, sweet drought-resistant herbage destined to fatten millions of cattle for the big cities on the Fringe.

Now she was here! the envy of her friends, a guest on one of the largest private cattle runs in the nation, carved out of virgin bush by one colourful young Englishman; a rugged individualist who nevertheless gloried in the pioneer life with all its dangers and privations. Paige had taken time out to read up about the tremendous feat that was 'Big John' Benedict's, a big man who deserved and found national recognition, a man who grew up with a powerful industry, exerting a far-reaching influence, for John Benedict was a man of vision!

At a time when most men thought he had gone off his head he had taken up his great selection. With *his* birth and breeding he could have become a big man; gone into politics, helped forge a new nation. Instead he had gone off on his big sorrel gelding on endless forays into the Big Country; and *this* at a time when the tribes were none too friendly and water was scarce. No one gave him much chance of coming back alive, though some, knowing the man, gave him a slight hope. He would have to work off his seeming obsession for the Back O'Beyond, the shimmering sunbaked plain with its cruelly misguiding mirage; a terrain, without a doubt, hostile to the white man.

'A man would need a heart like an elephant to overcome that!' they told him at Government House. He had *that* and its memory too! Nothing escaped him. Not a landmark, however slight. A man who left a trail in the desert had to know exactly where he was aiming for, his very life depended upon it. One thought was forever uppermost in his mind throughout his long wanderings. *Water*. Water for personal survival. Water, *permanent* water, to run his great herds of the future. Always and everywhere a man had to head for water or know how far off it was likely to be. The margin for safety was frighteningly narrow. The desert had known waterholes chartered by the explorers, many of whom died emaciated on the burning sands. But it had other waterholes known only to the aboriginals. These were the sacred watering places, and the brown man was not going to share his Dreamtime secrets with the white man.

So 'Big John' Benedict survived alone, a man living off wild country, aware of everything about him as only that kind of man can be. Years later he was quoted as saying: 'A man doesn't fight the Big Country, he learns to live along with it,' and he was the living proof of it as had been his brown brothers for countless centuries. The signs were there which might indicate where water could be found; the flight of birds, the tracks of animals, sandstone formation, certain plants that indicated ground water. Man, to survive, had to grow canny and careful, for a careless man was dead.

In this way he found his fabled El Dorado, the Three Rivers Country of the far South-West; the Channel Country with its maze of water-bearing streams and gullies, an elaborate network of irrigation channels that could carry flood waters from hundreds of miles off. It was here men of vision dreamed of a vast cattle empire with a future to fire any man's imagination. It had fired his! All through his long life Koombala remained closest to his heart, even though the Benedict chain linked up with the Territory and out to the Gulf. Now his grandson, Tyrone, stood at his elbow, ready to move into the seat of power. Paige shivered involuntarily, used to men of a gentler, more conventional breed. Koombala made a man different! On Koombala a man could look out over vast areas of bright green grasses and herbage clover a foot high, with stock standing thick upon it, all rolling fat. And it was *his*!

Even as she stood there watching and dreaming the fine flush of glory was leaving the sky. She turned away to bathe and dress for dinner, walking across the beautiful polished wood floor with its thick pile rug and opening the door softly. From somewhere she could hear the faint murmur of voices, the soft thud of a door. She turned back into her room and caught her questioning reflection in the mirror. In the pale golden light her eyes looked enormous, smoky blue, but there was nothing special or significant about that. She was excited, that was all. Who wouldn't be? Koombala was a legend. She was lucky to be here.

After a little reflection she laid out one of her prettiest frocks on the bed a sheer lemon dacron, floor-length, with an innocently seductive décolletage, tiny puffed sleeves and a wide yellow-gold sash. It was a dress a woman could be a woman in; a dress she frankly admitted made her feel 'just great' The little she had seen of Sonia Benedict, bone thin with elegant, blonde good looks, confirmed her previous impressions. She would be expected to 'dress' for dinner, exploding yet one more myth of Outback life.

Paige looked around her bedroom with pleasure. It was furnished with beautiful English traditional pieces co-ordinated with a clever contemporary touch in the soft furnishings. Her bed was huge! Canopied with a luxurious cream and gold quilt to match the side drapes. A magnificent writing bureau glowed like a jewel from a recessed corner; its glossy lacquer work entirely hand-done, as Sonia Benedict had explained to her with obvious pleasure in her guest's instant appreciation. It was decorated in the Chinese manner with gold leaf and iridescent gesso work; a 'little something'

Ty had picked up in his travels.

Just looking over the house had taken a good part of the afternoon. It was rather a curious house, much too big, as they all realized, but with a kind of awesomeness in its very dimensions. The rooms were vast, the ceilings high hung with the seeming incongruity of fairy-tale chandeliers 'Big John' had had shipped out from Home. They were eighteenth-century, with hundreds of pieces in the natural crystal, a touching attempt of a man to please his beautiful but fragile Surrey-born wife and a half sublimated desire for the old life. After all, a man had to impose some civilization on the wilds!

Paige smiled at these recorded words, knowing she would never forget Koombala, but its first mistress, Christina, had never been happy there. She had lived out her short life with gallantry, never complaining, but inwardly shrinking from the loneliness, the brutal splendour, the terror of flood and drought and marauding blacks, only to die in childbirth at the age of twenty-four, worn out by her efforts. Those were the days when a pioneer woman lived constantly with the threat of death, denied the life-saving techniques and facilities of a modern hospital.

Christina Benedict's son had survived her, as tough as his mother was fragile, with her raven-dark hair and emerald eyes but his father's great passion for a big, untamed land, a passion that was eventually to claim his life. 'Big John' had never remarried. Nor was he to be seen in the thrusting big cities for more than ten years. There were women, in plenty, none could deny that, but none he ever again made his wife.

Since those days the Big House had undergone many changes in redecorating and modernizing, but the chandeliers remained, though they attracted the moths in their millions, a tinkling, ghostly glittering reminder of the beautiful Christina, shedding light on her portrait that hung above the stairs.

Paige drew a deep breath and her heart thudded uncomfortably like some small fist inside her. She ran her bath with her head crammed full with thoughts, almost in chaos. So much seemed to be happening to her. Much later, standing in front of the mirror, she fiddled with a gold locket that her grandmother had worn as a girl. It seemed appropriate to the Big House, steeped as it was in the past. She leaned nearer the mirror and noted her bright colour, fastening the catch around her neck and saying to herself with simple understatement:

'You don't look too bad at all!' Her heart was beating so fast she almost had to put a hand to it, knowing deep inside her that she was not thinking wholly in terms of how Joel would find her. A few minutes later, with perfume touched to her ears and her wrists, she opened her door and slipped along the parquet corridor hung with old family portraits that silently appraised her, moving soundlessly towards the brilliant pool of light at the foot of the stairs. . . .

Dinner was nearing its end; the soup had been served, the plum-glazed chicken with butter-sautéed onion rings and deep coconut rice, and now Miri, the little aboriginal maid, was bringing in the passion-fruit mousse. She was a dusky appealing little creature, melting-eyed, very quick and neat in her movements. Sonia Benedict, in an ivory crêpe shift that fell in soft folds to her feet, helped herself to a tiny portion and returned to listening to Paige describing one of her more amusing fashion assignments. Under cover of the talk and light laughter Diane was unashamedly but sweetly absorbing every aspect of Paige's appearance.

Beside Tracey's sultry dark beauty she looked like a desert wildflower, delicate but beautifully tinted, very feminine, cool and serene. Joel, his sister had noticed, had never once taken his eyes from her face. So it was *that* serious! Only Ty sat back rather meditatively, his dark head tilted, green eyes guarded, a tiny smile touching the corners of his mouth.

'And how long ago was this?' Tracey broke in to ask Paige with a sourish smile and a variety of cruelty in her gleaming turquoise eyes.

Paige turned her head, a trifle disconcerted, for she considered the question irrelevant.

'Oh, well over a year ago,' she announced in her charming, low-pitched voice.

'I shouldn't care for that sort of thing at all,' Tracey shrugged a bare tan shoulder. 'I couldn't bear to be subjected to a nine-to-five routine. So demoralizing! cooped up like an animal in a cage.'

'Oh, quite!' Diane chirped in gaily. 'I know what you mean. It must be a martyrdom, a bind. Simply ghastly!'

Tracey appeared to find no fault in this. 'A woman should make up her mind early that she wants the best things out of life and go after them. She can, you know, if she uses her head.'

'There are millions who can't!' Joel retorted quite sharply, looking at Tracey with something approaching dislike.

'What use their heads?' Diane asked guilelessly, looking from one to the other.

'Well, it's their own fault if they can't!' Tracey hadn't even heard her glaring back at Joel with equal distaste.

Somehow Paige found her eyes settling on Ty's derisive smile. 'Not all the women in the world are obsessed with the best things in life, Tracey,' he said easily. 'Sawdust dolls are a dime a dozen!'

'Exactly!' Tracey looked mollified, as if he had with one stroke confirmed her opinion of their gauzy, extravagantly feminine visitor.

With a great effort Paige suppressed a smile, but Diane didn't.

'Tracey girl, you've done it again,' she said wryly. 'What you really need is a good matter-of-fact, informative article to read. "I fed a family of six on a hundred dollars a month!"'

'Rubbish!' Tracey's voice was sharp with conviction.

Sonia Benedict at the head of the table seemed isolated and quite above it all. 'Tracey dear,' she said mildly, 'do try and weigh your words more. If I thought for a moment you really believed half of what you say, I'd be really concerned!'

Tracey bit her lower lip and looked down.

'Oh, Mamma, but I adore you! Don't ever change!'

'You're good for me too, dear,' Sonia Benedict smiled back at her daughter, one fine golden-brown eyebrow taking an upward twist. Without so much as deigning to join the conversation Ty drained his wineglass and then turned to slowly refill Paige's glass.

'You'll be relieved to hear, Paige, that your first impression of the family is no more like them than a blurred photograph. Leave it for a couple of weeks before you judge us in all our dimensions.'

'Treason, by heaven!' Diane mocked him with a genuine between-the-two-of-us smile.

Sonia Benedict regarded her stepson with anxious eyes. 'Ty dear, surely you don't think. . . .'

Tracey tossed her sleek black head. 'It's me, Aunt Sonia,' she interrupted, glancing defiantly around the table. 'Please forgive me if I'm boring you all. I'll stop.' Her eyes swerved towards Paige and her tone lightened. 'That's a wonderful shade you get in your hair. What rinse do you use?' she asked at her gracious best.

'Oh, you rotten, awful kid!' Diane achieved, while her mother and brother looked grim.

'What's *your* excuse?' Tracey turned on her with heat.

'Why should a sweet little thing like you be so sour?' Joel demanded with such an edge to his voice that Tracey lost colour. Looking at her suddenly stricken face, Paige found it in her heart to be sorry for her.

'Might we with a little combined effort raise the standard of conversation at the dinner table?' Ty asked mildly. 'Nothing bores me more than pointless chitchat. All this can hardly be of any interest to Paige, and her a stranger to these parts,' he concluded with a sudden devastating grin that could rivet a woman's attention.

Paige looked away carefully, hearing Joel's voice:
'Yes, you girls, cut it out!'

'Anything, you know that!' his sister bounced right back.

'Talking to you seems a waste of breath,' he retorted, half amused, half irritated.

'For a midget she certainly packs a punch,' Ty agreed lazily, shooting back his cuff.

'I'm sorry, Ty. I'm afraid I started it all.' Tracey was all silky smoothness rather radically changing her style. 'It was all intended as a joke!'

It was such a palpable lie that Paige nearly laughed, then decided it didn't really matter that Tracey should so resent her.

Diane *did* laugh! 'It's all been a struggle, but it's paid off in the end,' she shot in as if she were only awaiting her opportunity.

'Do you want to go down in a jumbled heap?' Joel asked his sister, exasperated.

'What, punch or asphyxia?' she retaliated.

'Children! Children! Mind your manners,' Sonia Benedict said in a voice intended to squelch, 'though I fear they've gone beyond recall! Perhaps it's the heat?'

'All right, I'll say nothing at all.' Diane turned to her mother with her old affectionate expression. 'Ten minutes, no more!'

Paige suddenly gave her low gurgle of laughter that was oddly seductive and infectious at once and Diane turned to her with her greeny-grey eyes shimmering with impish light.

'Gosh, I wish I sounded like that!'

There was a soft insidious movement from Tracey across the table and Ty Benedict got leisurely to his feet all easy grace. Standing, he dominated them all.

'You'll excuse me, I hope,' he slanted a sardonic

sketch of a smile at Paige, 'on your first night, little one, but I have to have a word with my foreman before he turns in. Mustering starts in the pre-dawn before it gets too hot.' He smiled at his stepmother who was looking up at him expectantly. 'Coffee when I come back, Sonia. I'll get it, so don't bother.'

'No bother, dear, you know that!'

Paige found her eyes following the broad line of his back. He was a stranger, yet somehow he seemed more familiar to her than Joel who regarded her with warm hazel eyes. Coffee was served and Sonia Benedict spun them all into a gay web of talk, her thin, patrician face tolerant and confident. Occasionally Paige caught the few wry flickers that crossed her face at some of Tracey's less subtle jibes, but across the table she managed to convey to her guest a warm friendliness and approval.

Paige toyed with her beautiful tulip-shaped wine-glass, aware of the waves of resentment that encompassed her. Tracey looked very striking, very mettlesome, her long eyes enhanced by the blue-green of her dress, all hidden anger blotted out by a monumental indifference to Joel's 'latest passing fancy', her real feelings lighting a fire in her face and colouring the curves of her high, polished cheekbones.

After dinner Paige and Joel slipped away to linger in the cool of the verandah. The stars flowered in the purple sky, glowing with the unearthly white radiance that was peculiar to the desert. Bringah, the evening star, hung above them, a Dreamtime woman of unique magic, guide and guardian of young lovers. The Milky Way was densely strewn with daisies and above the soaring summit of the coolibahs at the bend of the river

Jirrunjoonga, the Southern Cross, dominated the sky.

It was a beautiful night, cool after the heat of the day, night birds thrilling to one another, the trees in the garden dark and impenetrable, alive with the mysterious sounds of the night, enhancing rather than detracting from the extraordinary miasma of peace and silence. Far off, following the night breeze, came the melancholy wail of a dingo pack, an eerie, shivery sound unique to Paige's ears which gave her a moment of sheer rootlessness and panic.

Joel turned to smile reassuringly at her. 'It's only dingoes on the prowl, city girl — disconcerting, I know but you'll get used to them.' He looked across at her, young, blondly handsome, very single-minded.

'I missed you, Paige. God, how I missed you!'

'Did you, Joel?' She smiled at him, the golden light from the hallway piercing the veils of shadows, caressing her rose-bronze head, her lambent eyes, outlining the singing line of her slender body.

'More than I ever dreamed!' He was suddenly behind her, his long fingers closing over the fine bones of her shoulders. 'Paige darling, your heart's beating fast!' His hand slid down over her shoulder.

'Joel!'

'Yes?' His voice was husky with longing and a slipping control.

'Please, Joel!'

'You're so beautiful, it seems like a miracle. I've never met anyone like you before. Please believe me. I love you. Not for today or tomorrow, but for ever. Please, darling, help me.'

She made a quick, movement, but he wouldn't stop.

'Joel!' she said breathlessly.

He released her with a tremendous effort, flinging his glance into her face challengingly with a faint edge of hostility.

'You don't love me, is that it? You've changed your mind?' His tones fell flat, reproaching her for her lack of response. His face had tightened under pressure; it looked older and harder.

She had a moment's apprehension at the explosiveness of the situation. Joel's profile became grim and taut.

'Please, Joel! You're not playing fair. You didn't ask me out to Koombala just to make love to me,' she stammered, not knowing which way to go on. 'That's not my way, Joel. I'm sorry, I'm sorry. . . .' She shuddered to a close, shocked by the force of his passion and her obvious reluctance to meet it.

'All right, all right!' his cheek hazed her hair. 'I'm the one who's sorry. It's just that I've never taken anyone so seriously before. Can you blame me for wanting to make love to you? You're so sweet, so softly seductive. Don't tell me it's wrong. Kiss me, Paige, please, with that lovely sensuous mouth. Paige, please. God, don't make me beg. . . .'

She turned up her mouth in a kind of drugged bewilderment, a tenderness, perhaps even . . . *compassion*? Joel lowered his head abruptly, his fingers bone white on her shoulders sliding down to crush her to him. It was like drowning, fighting to reach the cool air.

'Paige, there's so little time . . . Oh, God, sweetheart,

you're as smooth as silk!' His voice was insistent, rough with yearning. 'You care about me, don't you? Answer me, Paige!'

She pushed back against him, her head spinning, anxious in case someone should come out on to the verandah.

'Yes, I care about you, Joel,' she said gently. 'You know that!'

'I'm not at all sure I am. I should be, but I'm not. I'll tell you one thing, baby, I'll never let you go. Not ever. To anyone!'

In the silence that followed Paige felt as if she was standing on the edge of a precipice looking up at a stranger, a stranger with gleaming fanatical eyes, narrowed and fiercely intent upon her.

She made a small involuntary murmur of protest.

'Don't panic, sweetheart,' he said softly, reverting to himself again. 'I'm not going to ____ e a riot or anything. I've just got to admit you nave me tied up in knots!'

There seemed nowhere to withdraw to. She looked at him, then past him and at him again, her eyes enormous with a hint of distress.

He reached out a hand and brushed back her hair. 'There's a shadow in your eyes, Red!'

She touched the jumping pulse in her throat. 'I should explain to you, Joel,' she said carefully, 'I have a mind of my own.'

'Which means what?' he said jerkily.

Her eyes suddenly glowed, her quick temper surfacing. 'Applied to what you just said I exist in my own right. *My* wishes are important too, Joel.'

His eyes travelled over her cameo face, to her bare

shoulders, the lovely curve of her breast.

'Of course they are! But try to understand me, honey. I've been struck an all-time low. I want you. I need you, I'm damned if I can live without you!'

She stared up into his golden brown face, seizing on the possibility that he might be speaking the literal truth.

He cupped her face in his hands. 'Marry me, Paige!' She made no move to accept or withdraw and he kissed her mouth hard, almost a punishment. 'You'll have to give me a reason that doesn't exist. I'll give you everything you've ever wanted. One of these days, not too far off, I'm going to be a very rich man.' He suddenly shook her hard. 'If you loved me you'd say yes immediately. Here I am selling myself like a parcel of goods! If you only knew the damn girls . . . !' He broke off in a frenzy of irritation.

'Please, Joel, just a little time, that's all I ask.'

'Feeling the way I do about you it's pretty difficult to go slow. You're so beautiful, yet you're so cruel with it. You want to give so little.'

Her mouth seemed filled with a coppery taste. Joel would always take defeat hard, denied nothing from earliest childhood. What had been only a premise in her mind became an acknowledged fact.

'Whether I like it or not I've become obligated coming out here to Koombala, haven't I?' Her hands flew apart as if in recognition of the fact.

The saddened note in her voice sobered him. 'Don't *say* that! Don't ever say that. Hang it all, Paige, you act like I'm insulting you. You're a very mystifying girl, but I love you.'

'Well then, give me a little time, Joel. That's what I

thought this trip was all about – to get to know one another properly. Marriage is very easy to get into, but damned hard to get out of. That's the way I think, Joel. That's the way I am. I can't change. I must know my own mind.'

His gaze wavered, his face still with the intensity of his thoughts. 'Don't ever tell me a lie, that's all I ask.'

She looked up at him for a moment, startled. 'Can't we please talk of something else? All this is so futile. Don't let's argue my first night out.' Her soft mouth suddenly trembled and he was instantly contrite.

'Forgive me, Paige – that was what's known as the rushing technique. Obviously it failed. Now what about a nice cool drink? I'll make us something special. Just you sit there and wait.'

He took off rather fast, cursing his sore foot, giving her a backward raffish smile. 'Don't worry, Red. Everything will come right!'

Alone in the semi-darkness Paige was not so sure. Was she being dishonest with Joel? Dishonest with herself? On the other hand did she really have to make up her mind overnight? What was it Ty had said: *Don't let Joel steamroller you into anything you don't really want!* That was certainly his way. He was inclined to ride roughshod over her wishes. Why was it he seemed different on Koombala? In those first hectic weeks in the city just the thought of him had filled her with a pleasurable sense of anticipation and excitement. Yet here on Koombala when he looked, if possible, even more tall and handsome with a dashing out-of-doors insouciance, she knew this curious sense of withdrawal. His kisses were far from objectionable, in fact his sensual technique was very good. Perhaps this was a perverse, uniquely female reaction, a case approaching that of 'bridal jitters'. An iridescent insect caught in her hair and she was totally given over to removing it. Its gauzy wings came apart in her hand and she brushed her fingers quickly, fastidiously, looking out over the night-time enchantment.

There was a crunch of footsteps on pebbles and Ty Benedict stepped into the circular flood of light from the hallway. He came on up the stairs, not seeing her at first, wreathed as she was in the deep violet shadows. The light caught him full face and threw into strong relief his sculptured dark head and tanned face, the pale flash of his shirt now opened carelessly at the throat, the luminous green eyes, the third component in a colour scheme that was strikingly attractive.

She made a faint instinctive movement and his head turned with lazy affability. 'Hello there, flower face. How goes it?'

A faint shiver caressed her neck, then ran down her spine in a sweet shudder. She stood up and moved towards him, letting fall from her hand a profusion of red-gold berries from a blossoming shrub that cascaded over the iron lace railing. It was strangely redolent of passion-fruit, sweet but spicy.

His eyes ran over her flaring with strange lights. 'Well, you look like a girl who's been kissed senseless!'

It seemed to Paige that the very night was listening and assessing the effect of his words. She could feel herself flushing, but she kept an enviable hold on her voice.

'That's a staggering assumption. Might I ask how you arrived at it?'

He came a little nearer with lithe grace, very light-footed for a man of his size. 'Spare me, honey! I've been around. I know the score. What's wrong?'

She released a long-pent-up breath, slowly so he wouldn't notice. 'Nothing in the wide world. How could it be?' She threw him a glowing look, her eyes enormous.

He laughed without mirth. 'It's no guessing game. Your face tells me quite a lot.'

Her breath came in a soft gasp. 'You've no right to sound quite like that!'

'Haven't I?' He suddenly reached out and tipped up her chin. 'Koombala is my property. I feel a degree of responsibility for you. You don't know how young and alone you look.'

Her feathery dark brows lifted a fraction with sheer bravado. 'I might seem like that to you, but I assure you I do know how to look after myself. The city sophisticate, remember?'

His green eyes were coolly sceptical, glimmering between their thick dark lashes. 'That hasn't been my impression up to date. Maybe I'm old-fashioned, but little chicks like you bring out the protective streak in me – much as I hate it!'

'Yes, I can see that you might!' She looked out over the darkened garden, trying to give herself breathing space. She looked delicate, elusive, rather exotic, the pale stuff of her gown a wonderful foil for her hair.

His glance rested on her a trifle grimly as though he had reached a neat and conclusive opinion. 'You know, little one, country like this would break you, like it's broken a lot of women before you. It's essentially a frontier life, and you don't look a frontier lady!'

Her head tilted backwards and he saw her large, smoky eyes all ready to blaze into life. 'Are you trying to tell me to go away?'

'I'm not trying to tell you anything,' he said curtly. 'Not tonight, anyway, when you look more than a little distraught. Another time, maybe!'

'Tell me now!' she said imperiously.

'What?' His mouth relaxed in a half smile.

'Oh, don't play games with me, Ty,' she said huskily.

He gave her a smile that made her forget all thoughts of hostility. 'When you say my name like that! . . . Listen, little one, and listen well. You'd have to be very sure of your love for a man to contemplate living out here. The loneliness! Most women find it too hard to bear. A man has to be out so much of the time. He thrives on the life. . . .'

'A man like you,' she pointed out flatly, knowing that his face would be forever lodged in her mind, that aura of dark metalled pride.

'Joel's a cattleman too, honey. Don't forget!'

'Not like you!' she said almost beneath her breath, as if acknowledging a self-evident fact.

His voice when it came was terse. 'Paige, what *is* it you want? Do you know? You were very quiet at dinner. What was wrong?'

'I don't think Tracey likes me,' she smiled with ironic belief.

'Do good-looking women ever like one another?' he asked, deliberately evading the issue as he watched her with a gaze that was as disturbing as it was hard to analyse. He heard her sigh, caught the swift movement of her rose-bronze head.

'Joel once told me he'd like to manage a station of his own, nearer the central downs.'

He leaned back against the wrought iron railing, a brooding expression on his face. 'That can be arranged, in time. He still has a lot to learn.'

'But you don't think I'd make a good wife for him?' She didn't dare turn to look at him but sent her gaze winging out over the night-time jungle.

'No, I don't!'

She looked at him then, swiftly, involuntarily, stung by the brutality of the admission, the glitter of tears hanging on her eyelashes.

'Paige, you little fool!' He made an abrupt movement towards her, but was checked in his stride.

'Miz Benedict! Miz Benedict!' a wiry young aboriginal of about sixteen or seventeen raced towards the homestead steps yelling his head off, loud and clear. 'Miz Benedict?'

Ty rounded on him with barely concealed impatience. 'God damn it, Jimmy, you can sure make yourself heard! What is it, son?'

'Big trouble alonga way, Boss,' Jimmy said painstakingly slow, gasping for breath. 'Big feller colt got away!'

With one bound Ty cleared the railing the picture of winged outrage. 'You unholy menace! If you've been careless again, Jimmy, I'll wring your skinny neck!'

'More better you do that, Boss,' Jimmy's eyes were glassy with heat, 'but not plurry fair! One feller went right over the top. Like a plurry bird!' Jimmy's voice underwent a radical change, became comical, almost ready to give way to hilarity. 'Wow, whee! jus' like a blue crane. I nebber seen anything like it in me life!'

Ty bit off a half amused, half violent oath. 'Damnation, Jimmy, you'd laugh if you cut your toe off! Which way did the colt head?'

'Big sandhill country, Boss, I reckon!' Jimmy put his head on the side portentously, seeing 'the Boss' seemed to be over the worst.

'Next thing he'll be running with the brumby mob,' Ty murmured almost to himself. 'We'll have to go after him at first light. If he challenges Jumbali he'll finish up with a few scars.'

Paige moved over to the railing, smiling at Jimmy's startle. 'Evenin', Missy!'

'Who's Jumbali?' she asked with a leap of interest.

Ty turned back to her, his voice not matching his rather formidable face. 'The leader of the brumby mob,' he said mildly enough, 'a station stallion gone wild. *And* vicious! If the colt tries to take any of the mares off him he's in for big trouble.'

'Could I come?' She was conscious of a quick surge of excitement.

'No!' There was a world of masculine discrimination against her in that single syllable.

'That was unnecessarily blunt for mine host,' she said lightly.

He made a sudden swing back to her, very dark, very tall, very virile, a man in a man's country. 'Look here, little one, it would be a rough ride. I can show you, or Joel can show you the property at your leisure. That way you'll save yourself, and you have to learn how, especially in the heat.' He hesitated for a moment looking up at her, as colourful as a *namma gunta*, the beautiful Outback fairy butterfly. '*Can* you ride?' he asked with a sudden pulse of laughter in his black velvet voice.

'I've hacked about quite a lot. Oh, please, Ty!'

'Don't do it!' He spoke the words so caressingly that her heart jumped.

'What?' Her hand stole up to her throat, staring down at him.

'The Ty bit, as if you didn't know!' He looked away for a moment out over the silvered landscape, his dark face suddenly remote. 'All right then, you can come. We don't have any hacks on Koombala, but I might be able to find you a little filly with manners.'

'Marvellous – oh, Ty!' she smiled down at him, the sudden radiance in her face especially lovely. 'Thank you!'

'Don't thank me. Not yet!' he said tersely, his voice dubbing her hopelessly inexperienced. He turned round to Jimmy, an interested spectator. 'You can cut away now, Jimmy. Be up in the morning to saddle up the horses. You can come along with us if you like.'

'You plurry beaut!' Jimmy backed out of the light on soundless feet, leaving the lasting impression of glistening black eyes and a white, flawless smile. Paige felt like smiling herself.

CHAPTER SIX

THEY saddled up at pre-dawn when the mother-of-pearl sky was showing the first faint flushes of light – Ty, Joel, Tracey and Paige with Jimmy bringing up the rear. Paige glanced across at Joel's vaguely hostile profile. He sat his horse in a relaxed, easy manner, gracefully slouched, favouring his sore foot. He was none too pleased with her, she could tell, but adamant about accompanying them out. They had indulged in a quick spate of words the previous night. Paige could still hear Joel's hot, resentful tones, but surprisingly enough their disagreement only strengthened her desire to go after the colt; in the process seeing a great deal of Koombala. Something in her craved to get moving, to see as much as she could of the Outback, and Joel's distinctly proprietorial manner had rankled.

Tracey, a late entry in the chase, in beige tailored riding pants and a crisp cotton shirt with a blue and green bandana at her throat, looked the professional horsewoman, confidently holding in her big black gelding with a white diamond blaze and one white stocking. Her long eyes gleamed with a kind of malicious satisfaction at Paige's vastly inferior technique, but Paige didn't mind. She stroked her beautiful little filly's chestnut coat, enjoying the sensation of being in the saddle and the crystal clarity of an Outback morning. They rode down the shady banks of the lagoon as the sun rose higher in the eastern sky and cleared the rose-red bluffs of the Big Sandhill Country. It was deliciously cool, the whole world alive with the darting swiftness of birds and the wind song. Flower swallows circled above them, blue and crimson, the little painted finches, the great flights of budgerigar, green and golden. Some way off in the distance women's voices wafted to them; chattering and laughing young lubras collecting their favourite delicacy – wild honey.

Joel reined in alongside her, smiling for the first time that morning.

'You're doing very well, Paige Norton. In no time at all we'll make another Tracey of you. She can handle anything. Born to it, of course. It does make a difference.'

Paige's eyes swept ahead over Tracey's strong, slender back. Her golden-skinned profile was turned towards Ty, her long turquoise eyes shaded by the wide brim of her cream stetson. This morning she looked a different girl, vivid and confident, living the life for which she was pre-eminently suited. Paige's glance stayed on her for a long moment, deeply reflective

'She's very fond of you, Joel!' she found herself saying with no prior intention of saying any such thing.

A smile split Joel's mildly scandalized face. 'No kiddin'! God, sweetheart! Tracey and I have been at one another's throats ever since I can remember. She was a dreadful child. You can't know how awful! Her parents' fault, maybe. They were at loggerheads, always on the point of divorce right up until they literally crashed. More often than not Tracey was used as a whipping post. When she arrived on Koombala she was impossible – and I mean impossible! A conniving little brat who brought Di and me nothing but trouble. Mother, of course, took her to her heart like one of her own. Wouldn't listen to our complaints, or not many of them, at any rate.'

A faint tenderness touched Paige's mouth. 'Your mother's a wonderful woman. I very much admire her!'

'*And* she likes you too, sweetheart! That makes me very happy. I don't care to go against my mother's wishes if I can help it.'

'Well, that's a nice thing about you!' Paige smiled into his eyes, then looked up ahead, narrowing her eyes against the brightening sunlight. They were skirting a gorge of red rocks where butterflies clustered in their dozens, Chinese blue, black and yellow, then on to the red, scrub-clad sandhills lined with white-boled lime-woods, kurrajongs and napunyah trees. What was it Ty had said: Once it gets a hold of you it captures you forever! She could see it very well might. She glanced back at Joel riding contentedly by her side.

'Poor Tracey! She rides beautifully, doesn't she? And she looks very happy this morning. It can't have been easy for her as a child. They say you never forget the formative years.' She flung him an impish smile. 'She's very good-looking, too – a fact you didn't think fit to mention. In fact from your description I might have been forgiven for thinking she had squint eyes.'

Joel laughed aloud. 'She may be good-looking, but when it comes to being a *female* female she could take lessons from you!'

'Perhaps you're not treating her right?' Paige ventured, returning his bright stare.

'Give it a while before you start throwing stones,' he

answered laconically.

A few hundred yards away a rabbit suddenly popped out of its hole almost under the feet of Ty's beautiful but temperamental cream and gold stallion. It reared and plunged wildly, the wind catching its flowing plume and long tail and transmuting them into shafts of ivory silk. Paige felt her breath caught in her throat. It was visually heart-stopping, exciting her into an emotional response. The man, the rearing horse starkly etched against the peacock sky, seemed the very embodiment of untamed splendour; the splendour of the land itself. She scarcely heard Joel's next words; so preoccupied was she that he covered her hand on the reins.

'I'm sorry about last night, Red!'

'That's all right, Joel,' she answered almost abstractedly as she watched Ty quiet his mount, talk to it gently, regain control. 'Let's forget it!' she turned away to smile at Joel. 'I can quite understand your feeling tied down, with your foot.'

'Damn my blasted foot!' Joel said irritably. 'It's nearly better anyway. It was more the thought of your gallivanting over the countryside with the Crown Prince!'

Paige digested this piece of information in silence – her own conclusion in any case. 'Why do you call Ty the Crown Prince?' she asked, ignoring the main bone of contention.

'Because that's what he is, girl,' he bit off soberly. 'What do you make of him?' He walked his horse through the Mitchell grass, avoiding the ground parrots that foraged after the seed. 'Well?' he suddenly shot her a glinting stare.

'I quite *like* him!' Paige announced casually with charming deceit, privately thinking that Ty Benedict wasn't a man who incited any such milk-and-water reaction.

'*Like* him!' Joel tasted each word, then subsided with a grin. ' 'Struth, that's one up on Ty!' Paige's eyes and her voice, had she known it, would have done credit to an actress of talent. They satisfied Joel. He took a deep breath and filled his lungs with the dry spicy air.

Paige smiled. 'It's beautiful, Koombala!' she said with sincerity. 'Strange and oddly beautiful.'

'It's that!' Joel said briefly, his golden-brown face tautening. 'It's Ty's, you know, or to put it another way, Ty *is* Koombala, the controlling force and motivating spirit. His son will inherit, not mine.'

'Does the thought distress you, Joel?' She turned on him compassionate eyes.

'It does a little!'

'You'd be less than human if it didn't,' she pointed out ironically.

Joel seemed to brighten. 'When we're married, we'll have our own station. The Benedict chain is pretty far-reaching. Have you ever been out to the Central Downs?'

Paige shook her head, thinking the conversation was going too far ahead again. 'No!'

'It's beautiful there, too,' Joel said calmly. 'More what you've been used to. The South-West is unique in the world, an unforgettable landscape, even if you don't like it. The fiery red sandhills, the glitter off the gibber plains, the legends of a Timeless Land; Marat-joora, the desert, even the blue flame mirage. Still . . .

that's that! He threw up an expressive hand, and continued, 'Now *we* could spend a lot of our time on the coast. Any city you liked. I could put a manager in. Come to think of it, we could go around the world on our honeymoon. There are still a lot of places I haven't seen. Besides, I want to show you off.' His eyes lightened and brightened with amusement. 'Grandfather would love you! Even at eighty he's still got an eye for a pretty woman. Ty's Big John all over again. I guess that's why the Old Man idolizes him, though the two of them fall out pretty often.'

'They do?' Paige turned on him startled eyes. This was news!

'Good God, yes!' Joel said with some satisfaction. 'They've had any amount of ding-dong battles in the past. Ty goes his own way, you know even if Grandfather *is* the Cattle King. Nowadays Ty takes it pretty easy. Big John's an old man, though it's hard to credit . . . or accept.'

'Where does he live?' Paige asked.

'Melbourne, mostly. The financial heart. We see him pretty often. One of his staff usually flies him out. He goes on periodic tours of the chain, taking Ty along with him. That's if Ty *wants* to go.' Joel chuckled at some wry thought. 'I've got to hand it to him, Ty kowtows to no one. I wouldn't care to cross the Old Man myself. Not in a million light years!' His eyes scanned her creamy-skinned face shaded by the stylish wide brim of her black gaucho hat. 'By now he'll have heard on the grapevine about you! He keeps us all pretty well under surveillance. A good thing you're not Ty's chosen bride – you'd get an almighty once-over! Big John's got a thing about "the right kind of woman",' he mimicked his grandfather's still 'English' tones. 'Never picked one himself, but it's a case of don't do as I do . . . or else!'

Paige drew a deep breath, a hyacinth sheen caught in her eyes. 'Perhaps he'll come down strongly against me. Have you thought of that?'

Joel gave a wry snort. 'No problem there, sweetheart. I'm not the Crown Prince. It does have the occasional compensation!'

'Hmm, that might be!' Paige smiled at the touch of irony. They rode along in a companionable silence while high above them soared a wedge-tailed eagle on the constant look-out for prey. Ahead of them lay the big game country of the far south-west, the ancient hunting grounds of the aborigine. They fell into line to cross a narrow stone-ringed gully fringed by the secret, shrub-shrouded caves of Paraloo, the dingo. It was an eerie place; the meeting place for the native initiation rites. Out in the sun again Paige felt blinded by the brilliant earth patterns, the Namatjira-red sand, in startling contrast to the vivid green of the shrubs and vines.

The horses moved easily over the sandy ground, disturbing a flock of parrots that lay along the flower-decked branches of the acacias. They rose with shrill notes, showing their remarkably long tails; opal-tinted, pale yellow, green and blue, with pink around the eyes, the throat and the breast.

'*Noorinna Nahlen!*' Joel gave them their native name. 'The Princess Alexandra parrots. Beautiful, aren't they? But what a din!'

Paige smiled and swayed around in the saddle, her slender, supple figure drooping a little. It was getting on towards mid-morning and the sun seemed to be leaping at her, catching at her dry throat. It poured down from the peacock sky; a molten gold glory. Never in her life had she experienced such a quality of light. Paige adjusted the wide brim of her gaucho hat to a rakish angle, conscious that the sun was catching the vulnerable nape of her neck. Jimmy, scouting up ahead, came back at a flying gallop shouting something quite incomprehensible to Paige but readily understandable to the others. They followed him up in pursuit, their faces betraying a uniform elemental excitement.

Paige spurred her little filly on, relieved beyond words at its swift, intelligent response. On the crest of a fiery red sandhill, they came on a wonderful sight – a mob of wild horses sentinelled against the sun, ringed round by a fiery aureole. Centred among them and slightly to the front was their leader, a big bay gelding of a good seventeen hands with deep shoulders, a long arching neck and powerful legs: Jumbali the Outlaw. Only a moment, then they wheeled and galloped, pounding across the spinifex flats, tails and manes flying in the wind of their own motion. At a safe distance the mob stood their ground, ranged behind their leader, Jumbali, who was snorting and pawing the ground, wide mouth flecked with foam, a rage of independence burning in his white-ringed eyes.

He looked *bad*! Paige thought, and controlled a nervous shudder. Suddenly the big bay whirled with viciously slashing hoofs, biting and lashing, spurring on the mares who milled and ran screaming with rage and fear.

Paige touched a hand to her head. The sun and the

excitement seemed to be too much for her. She felt lightheaded with the beginning of a bad headache. To her relief Ty decided to let the mob go, satisfied that the colt was not running with them. In another half hour Paige was bitterly regretting her own foolhardiness. She wasn't the 'jillaroo' type, but not for anything would she admit it. Tracey would be too damned patronizing by half if the party were obliged to call a halt. She gave Joel a bright smile that cost her an effort as she watched him ride into the lignum that ran along a seven-mile chain of half-filled billabongs. Tracey followed him up, beating at the bush with a stick in an attempt to flush the colt out should he have gone into hiding. There seemed to be no sign of Ty, Paige thought distractedly. He must have followed Jimmy up, for the aboriginal boy had his own line of bushcraft.

Her skin felt cold and clammy when the heat was reaching out to envelop her. She felt extremely fatigued, faintly dizzy. She would rest a little in the shade of the blossoming bauhinias. The clusters of flowers were pure white, little dazzling trumpets of light. If only she could reach the shade . . . the shade. . . . She rode towards it almost blindly, skirting the clumps of big old man saltbush that stood up in softest grey mounds. Along all the seven-mile stretch there was permanent water. Perhaps she could bathe her face. The branch of a feathery little acacia tickled her face.

'Paige!'

A harsh, clipped voice shocked her back to full sensibility. She lifted her head to look into Ty's teak-tanned face, the quick lick of flame from his eyes. Her creamy-skinned face had a pronounced pallor heightened by apricot sunspots that stained her cheeks. Her eyes were huge and distressed, a little trickle of perspiration running from a blue-veined temple.

'God!' He took hold of her reins and she submitted without a word, letting him lead the filly towards the green shade, threading a path through the scattered acacia bushes, the gidgee and the coolibah saplings, down sloping banks to a moon-shaped lake.

Lotus blooms stood up in a violet haze flanked by tall reeds with cane grass clumps ringing the banks overhung with bush willows. At their approach, waterfowl took wing, swirling up to the trees that showed chinks of brilliant blue light. It was a green, remote world that silently meditated, dappled with sun and shadow. The temptation to remain there forever was almost irresistible.

Ty dismounted without a word, his face a hard mask, his hands warm and vibrant as he lifted her from the saddle, keeping a steely grip on her arms. Behind them the horses fell to cropping over the tender shoots of cane grass. His glance was comprehensive, anger in every taut line of him. He pushed her hat back off her head, while her bright head lolled slightly on its fragile neck.

'I'm all right,' she said huskily, unsteadily, into the verdant silence. 'Truly I am!'

'The hell you are! You look completely fuddled.' His voice held the level tones of cool anger. He half led, half carried her down towards the shimmering water.

She tried to shake him off fretfully. 'Please, Ty. You needn't stay with me. I won't bother you. I'm all right.'

'Be quiet!' He pulled the strap of her black gaucho hat over her head and flung it back on to the sand with a wholly masculine impatience. 'If you didn't look so pale and defenceless I'd beat you. Haven't you the sense to know when you've had enough? No, you'd never give in! Pigheaded, redheaded little scrap, making yourself thoroughly miserable in the process.'

'Oh, you're horrible!' She drew a long quivering breath.

'I *am* horrible, and I want my head read. It's my fault anyway. I should never have let you come!' He broke off, the expression on his dark face excessively irritated.

Paige watched languorously as he withdrew a large clean handkerchief from his pocket and bent to the stream. She retreated a little, but he caught her face in his hand, wiping it clear, holding the cold cloth for long moments over her forehead, not caring in the least for the trickles of sweet, brackenish water that ran down the deep V of her shirt. He tilted her head back and she was forced to accept his administrations like a child. Yet it was strangely reassuring, the knowledge that a man's strength was, at times, sufficient unto itself. Her eyelids fluttered down, unable to meet the green glance that told her he was irritated beyond measure with the smallness and the slightness of her, the disconsolate droop of her head.

She heard him give an exclamation of muffled impatience, then she was lifted in his arms as he carried her back towards the thick carpet of cane grass. She sank back against it, enveloped in its fresh, faintly prickly softness. For a few moments there was silence, then she heard his voice with a suggestion of roughness in it.

'Drink this!' She opened her eyes and they settled helplessly like a moth on his mouth. It was a mouth whose outline was growing too personal, too painfully disturbing. Heat surged through her veins and she shut her eyes again with a sigh. It was so deliciously cool in this secret, silent place, so far removed from the flaring heat. Her creamy pale face was utterly still as if she were already on the borderline of sleep.

'Paige!' In another minute she was brought upright by his hand hard at her back, forcing her to drink a long draught of pure, cold water from his canteen.

Her parched throat was immediately eased. 'Thank you!' she said like a polite child, as moisture dewed her soft mouth.

'You're welcome, little one.' His face softened slightly with satire. He screwed the top of the canteen on carefully, then pushed her gently back into the grass. 'Relax. You're always so tense. Try to relax. You'll come to no harm.' His eyes were intent on her, as cool and compelling as the glitter off a rock-pool.

'Are you trying to hypnotize me?' she asked faintly.

'I am!' The half ironical little catch of laughter was back in his voice again. 'There's a tiny hammer going here at the base of your throat.' He touched a lean finger to it and her skin tightened electrically and her smoky eyes dilated. He looked down at her, his eyes narrowing. 'You little fool!' his voice was a mere thread of sound. 'What are you expecting? The wild colonial boy?'

'I'm not expecting anything,' she said in a breathless

protest. 'What do you mean?'

'Drop it, honey,' he said tersely. 'You're afraid to wake up.' His voice had the cutting edge of metal, flicking her raw sensitivity.

'I'm in a damnable position, aren't I?' she said in a flat, dejected voice.

'Yes, you *are*!' He turned to half smile at her with deepest irony. 'But you're definitely not running away! Close your eyes, little one,' he said wearily. 'You're safe enough for a half hour or so.'

She flushed under his mocking gaze and lay back. 'It pleases you to taunt me,' she said softly. 'I wonder why?' She closed her eyes and caught the drift of warm fragrance from his cigarette, hearing the sizzle of the spent match, the quick stamp of his foot. The wildest notions began to fill her head, but she struggled against them. There was an aura of fantasy about the whole thing. The trees were awhisper with a ceaseless chitter-chatter, the jewel-flashes of wings. A lovely wash of light filtered greeny-gold through the trees, the wind-song fluting through the reeds. Water. Peace. Absolute peace . . . of a kind! She visibly relaxed, the sweet grass tickling her cheek, the throbbing in her temples abating. Already her eyelashes, thick and heavy, were settling on her cheeks. . . .

A shadow fell across her body and her eyes flew open in a panic. She was completely disorientated, shock playing havoc with her heart. The smell of crushed grass came into her nostrils mingled with the scent of the native boronia, the wild lime. It was the shriek of a sulphur-crested bird that had awakened her. It noisily flapped its wing and swung to and fro on the gidgee.

Ty still sat slightly above her, a glittery look on his face. His eyes seemed to have caught the colour and the sheen of the leaves; brilliant yet vivid. She looked into them for a brief, drowning moment, desperately fighting her way out of the soft waves of yearning that threatened to engulf her. Her very flesh seemed to be dissolving, odd little tremors flicking up and down her spine.

'Ty!' She said his name with a soft hesitancy, almost in a dream, more subtly exciting than deliberate provocation would ever have been. His face seemed carved out of teak, still and ... *waiting.* Her eyes deepened and darkened under his gaze, the pupil expanding. A subtle transformation had come into her face, spinning threads of awareness between them goading him as a man, into the deepest appreciation of her heightened femininity and beauty; the slender young body that was so marvellously constructed for loving, her ability to stimulate desire.

His voice came in a soft rasp: 'Paige!'

Her delicate nostrils flared and her mouth, tender and sensuous, shaped itself a single word of defence.

'No!'

'No?' His brief laugh was harshly disbelieving. He slipped a hand under her bright hair to shape her creamy nape. 'No, rainbow bird, when everything about you is crying out to be made love to?'

The touch of his hand was an intolerable stimulant from which she tried to jerk her head wildly. He held her still, faintly increasing the pressure. 'No, don't fight me. The experiment begins. On my own land and in my own time!' His face had a hard, disturbing charm about it, the arrogance of a man who knew exactly what he wanted and the best way to get it.

He lowered his head and she shuddered, a slender reality in his arms, shocked and shaken, her pulses thundering, arriving at the core of her individual existence. His mouth, his driving masculinity, closed over her like a dark, golden storm ... and then she was clinging to him ... clinging to him ... outside of herself, while her body in betrayal fitted itself to the lean shape of him; an exquisite pain.

It was a feeling no language could express, white-hot and mysterious, flowing on and on in her like the wind and the bird song, the magical quality of light itself. They might have been alone in a green world, complete, self-sufficient, mindless of reality. It was a moment she could live over and over again and each time it would be the same ... a physical radiance that would come back to haunt her every time she closed her eyes. She didn't know she was murmuring his name incoherently against his mouth.

His hand thrust through her hair tugging her head backwards, his voice hard and taunting with a strange look of power.

'Never tell me you're in love with Joel. Right now you're not ready to love anyone!'

Her heart leapt in her breast at the cynical sparkle in his eyes. 'Love is a strong word, Mr. Benedict,' she said raggedly. 'I've never told Joel that I *do* love him. In fact, right now, I don't believe that I could ever love anyone!'

His white smile was hard and derisive, completely devoid of mirth. 'I can pretty well forget everything you *say*,' he said cruelly.

'And why is that?' she hurled at him, her slender

back arching like a cat. 'Ty Benedict, you arrogant green-eyed philanderer, go on and answer me!'

He only held her down, amused at her impotence. 'Far from being a philanderer, my smoky-eyed not-so-innocent, experience has taught me to tread damned warily with women. Especially the ones with lotus eyes!'

There was no tenderness in him, she could see that now. Only a passionate nature that could carry a woman along like a spring tide. She was breathing quickly, her slight breast rising and falling, still half lying against him, for he made not the slightest attempt to release her. The atmosphere between them was brittle with a new tension as if they were emerging from a painful quarrel.

She suddenly beat a small fist to his shoulder, the tumult in her veins transmuted to a defiant fury. 'Let me go, you conceited devil!'

'In a moment, flower face!' He held her wrist in the air with careless strength. 'There's one small point that requires elucidation. Just whose girl are you?'

Her response was immediate, the sudden blaze in her eyes quite remarkable. 'I'm nobody's girl! You believe it, Ty Benedict, though it's no small thing to gain your all-exclusive attention.'

'Oh, you've got *that* all right!' His own eyes were brilliant, taut pressure lines about his mouth, his drawl insolent. 'But you haven't really answered my question.'

Her brain cleared miraculously. 'I never tell a man anything unless I absolutely have to!' she tossed off in a brittle, sophisticated voice. 'It's the number one rule!'

Strange leaping lights danced in his eyes. He looked

quite capable of cruelly jerking her to her feet, ignoring her small cry of pain, shackling her wrist. 'You play it pretty close to the cuff, don't you, lotus eyes?'

'I have to!' she said crisply.

'Ah, a professional!' A brilliant hostility and a lurking devil flared into his eyes. For a moment she knew what it was like to be frightened of a man.

'My God, that was detestable!' she said wildly, an ache starting up in her breast, the salt of tears in her throat. 'But then you *are* detestable, aren't you?'

'Am I?' His fingers bit deep into her skin. 'I have to admit there's some aspect of your personality that eludes me.'

She threw up a beautifully posed head. 'Complications are the spice of life, Mr. Benedict,' she said with amused contempt. 'I thought you knew that!'

He jerked her b̲ ̲ᵈ up against him with a sort of savage fury that brought the overwrought tears to her eyes. 'One more word and I'll teach you a lesson you won't forget!'

She swallowed on her tears. 'I believe you mean that!'

He ignored the diamond drops that glittered on her lashes. 'You're learning!' Suddenly his hand gripped her shoulder, an urgent expression on his face, his attention stunningly diverted. 'Be still!'

Behind them the horses stopped cropping over the grass and lifted their heads as one. The filly gave a low, soft whinny and Paige froze. An echoing call floated back along the reed bed, where the tall grasses were stirring. Paige stood perfectly still, as motionless as a small golden statue. Intuitively she foresaw what was coming, her scalp prickling with anticipation. Ty's hand was still biting into the delicate hollow near her collarbone, but he seemed unaware of it, his dark face graven, only the eyes moving.

'The colt!' he said beneath his breath, willing it to come on with power and concentration.

There was silence for a few moments, then the soft trumpeting call of the male. On and on the colt came, thirsting for the sweet waters of the lake; a beautiful thing, its ebony coat rippling over muscles of sprung steel, a contrasting mane and tail of streaming silver. Red dust dappled its flanks and shoulders; it had been running hard. Out of the corners of its eyes it caught sight of them, freezing into the instinctive stillness of an animal that scents danger. The filly of its own accord picked its dainty way down the banks and moved towards the stream, the sun firing her chestnut coat. She whinnied again and the colt came right out into the open, arching its graceful neck up and down, stamina and virility written all over him. Paige felt her senses tightening. Horses were such temperamental animals. One never knew where one was with them.

Ty let the silence rest for a while, then he gave a low whistle of extreme melodiousness. The colt threw up his head, tense with nerves. Paige shut her eyes, finding the suspense unbearable. In another minute the colt would take to reckless flight. Ty's hands had left her shoulders. He was no longer behind her, then she heard his voice a little way off, so caressing he might have been half speaking, half crooning the words of a lullaby.

She opened her eyes cautiously. Ty was now standing a few feet from the colt, the advantage still with him, while the colt seemed to listen to what he was saying with a proud dignity. The quiet talk went on until finally Ty went right up to the animal and ran his hand over its black satin side. He spoke over his shoulder with precisely the same tone of voice, just pitched to reach her ears.

'Move very quietly and pass me my saddle rope. Don't worry about Bega, he's well trained.'

Paige found she was trembling. Step by step she made her way back up the bank to the gold and cream stallion. It swished its long tail and turned its shining muscled body. She unhooked the rope and made her way down to Ty as soundlessly and as unobtrusively as a shadow. He took the rope from her, keeping one hand on the colt's neck, then he slipped the noose over the high-spirited head and watched it settle neatly around the neck. Gently he kept talking and stroking the trembling animal which gradually quietened, exhaling a gusty breath.

'Steady, my beautiful!' His face was a study in pride possession.

Paige's own face was faintly amused. A woman couldn't have asked for a more tender tone. Did he reserve it only for his horses?

Ty turned his head and tilted a black eyebrow. 'I'll say one small thing for you, little one, on the odd occasion you keep your head!'

She made a wry grimace at the same old mocking tone. 'A girl can only swim with the tide. It requires a level head.'

Half smiling, he walked the colt on, allowing it to drink a moment at the stream. 'Better make it back to the others,' he said laconically. 'We'll head straight on home.'

His face was lit by a glimmer of devilry, a trace of ironic humour. 'It's as well we've got the colt to show for ourselves! Joel will be as wild as a hawk!'

Her eyes, huge and questioning, met his across the colt's silver mane.

He lifted one black eyebrow, a saturnine cast to his face. 'Don't worry, flower face,' he said casually. 'All's well that ends well . . . so they say!'

Without a word Paige turned away from him and walked up the bank to saddle up. She didn't trust Ty Benedict in any mood. Mocking, ironical, laughing . . . making love!

CHAPTER SEVEN

Spring turned into summer with days so still and bright that the blueness of the sky hurt the eye. Each morning a beautiful dawn broke with massed cloud piled up in the north, only to melt at the first touch of heat. There were no thunderstorms, only agate bright evening skies that faded into amethyst. But each day they waited, all of them, anxiously scanning the sky. Nuljiri, the old eagle-hawk warrior, toothless and shaking his head dolefully, predicted no rain for that season, pointing his spear to the sky where legions of budgerigars darkened the sun with the emerald flash of a million wings. Nankeen plovers followed the racing whirlwinds, circling and diving in a mad ecstasy, '*a bad omen*', Nuljiri said, for these were the birds that revelled in drought.

The three-mile lagoon facing the Big House was still green and beautiful, thrusting with waterlilies, a clear sheet of water that had never been known to go dry, but the smaller chain of waterholes were beginning to dry up, forcing the cattle to crowd around the permanent holes and the bores eating out the surrounding grasses. Out on the sandhills the hardy standby in drought years, the spinifex, was turning under the hot sun from yellow to brown, and for a careless stockman to drop a match meant instant dismissal. They all knew that and accepted it. The fear of fire was burned into all of them.

The great herds on Koombala were still holding condition, but the cows and their calves were being moved only during the night hours or in the pre-dawn to avoid hardship. The entire central and southern belt was drought-stricken and the old hands were forecasting a big cattle crash. Koombala in the sixty thousand square mile complex of the Channel Country of the far south-west had two things in its favour: four thousand square miles of saltbush and lignum flats and a sixty-mile front on to the Diamantina. The Promised Land after flood, it was, with the aid of bores, all but drought-proof.

Not so Mundoora, a link in the Benedict chain, four hundred miles to the north-east, right in the centre of the drought belt. In times of adversity were the great benefits accruing from a chain most quickly apparent, for each station worked in co-operation with the chain for the good of the whole. On Koombala, the men began working long hours mustering the fats to get them on to the road, leaving water and grass for a mob of two thousand strong to be sent, under Ty's instructions, to Koombala.

For over a week he was away at Mundoora, flying on to Bogabilain, another Benedict link in the lush Gulf country, making arrangements for that big, isolated station to take another few thousand head from the drought-stricken centre. Old Man Drought could wield his whip, but somehow the Benedict chain would make out.

Every one of them in some way felt his absence. For Joel increased responsibility and less free time, for Paige a kind of limbo of suspension. As the weeks had slipped past, she had settled into a routine that wonderfully agreed with her, dividing her time between the house, the green oasis of the garden, Sonia's undisputed province, and endless forays into the Big Country with Di or Joel as a companion. Even on the odd day when Tracey had consented to accompany them the trips were successful, for Paige, had she known it, was succumbing to a spell; the call of the Never-Never. On the few occasions she had mentioned the foreseeable end of her holiday, Sonia Benedict had thrown up her hands. Under no circumstances would Paige be allowed to return under three months, the full period of her leave of absence. After all, the whole purpose of the visit was for her to get to know the family and familiarize herself with Joel's background his way of life. Whatever decision they arrived at, and Sonia never pried, Paige was a most welcome guest.

So Paige stayed on, finding in Sonia and her daughter a rewarding companionship, in Joel an ardent but frustrated lover, in Tracey a combatant in a cold war. It took no extra perception on Paige's part to realize that Tracey would always withhold her friendship, waiting only for the day when Paige would leave Koombala ... without Joel!

But from Ty she had to remain aloof. That was her only safeguard. It came to her swiftly with a thrust of pain that this was a mutual move, for Ty had retreated behind a cool but inpenetrable reserve. It was better so! Her head told her so, but now on his first evening home from Bogabillain she had the bitter realization that her treacherous senses would always let her down. Ty was Ty, with a matchless dark vitality. She folded a pleat in her amber-coloured silk, letting it fall with a soft sideways swish to the floor. She turned her body slightly picking up her wineglass, the fabric of the tiny bodice of her gown tightening over her breasts, her small waist. In her hyacinth eyes lingered a moment of doubt. Her old self seemed to have drained away like liquid in a wineglass; like water between stones. This disconcerting self-alienation gave her still creamy face a haunting effect, as sadness often enhances beauty. Across the table she met Tracey's long turquoise stare, realizing, not for the first time, that Tracey had her under constant surveillance, seeking the flaw.

She ate very sparingly, though the food was delicious, listening, sometimes joining the conversation that ranged over a wide number of subjects but inevitably returned to the affairs of the station and the state of the country to the north. Looking down the table at Ty's handsome dark head she decided he looked just the same, but on closer observation found she was wrong. He had lost weight, the lines from nose to mouth were more pronounced, a faint air of preoccupation about him, almost a kind of severity.

He lifted his head quickly and smiled, transforming his face and throwing a teasing glint into his green eyes.

'Well, what's the verdict, young Paige?'

'I was thinking the same thing myself!' Tracey observed, giving a tinkle of laughter at odds with the censorious look in her eyes.

'Enlighten us, kiddo,' Diane smiled.

Paige coloured a little, a wry smile touching her mouth. 'I'm sorry, I suppose I *was* staring. I just thought you'd lost a little weight, Ty.'

He kept his head turned to her, his eyes suddenly sparkling. 'Maybe a pound or two,' he agreed with a smile. 'If you think it's hot here, little one, you should have come along with me. I've been fighting fires a good part of the time, burning breaks around Mundoora homestead and the yards. The conditions there, at the moment, are appalling. Fresh fires break out every day. In the intense heat it's inevitable, God knows. The heat breeds whirlwinds and the whirlwinds carry strips of flaming bark for hundreds of yards. They only have to hit the resinous wattles . . .' He made a small, sharp movement of his hand, clenching the fist with leashed power, and continued: 'Bob and the boys are completely worn out,' a sudden grimness touched his mouth. 'Fires in the ranges, fires across the run. The whole time I was there the sun was blanketed with a cloud of smoke. I hope to God they don't have any more setbacks. If we don't have rain soon and the wind gets behind a fair-sized fire it'll sweep through the entire run with the speed and ferocity of lightning. The whole place would be gutted. No one could cope with it.' He looked beyond Paige to Joel. 'Incidentally, we'll burn a few breaks ourselves.'

'Do you think that's necessary?' Joel asked with a faint look of surprise on his face.

'I do!' Ty said briefly, and that settled it. From the look on his face he was in no mood to argue the point over, and Joel obviously didn't care to risk it.

Ty lifted his head again, his eyes straying to Paige. The lights from the brilliant overhead chandelier struck flames from her hair. 'A strange thing about fire,' he said with mingled anger and fascination, 'it can be incredibly beautiful. On Mundoora, by daylight, a blackened desolation, by night . . . so damned beautiful! Bob and I rode along a seven-mile front with countless burning trees coming down cascading brilliant showers of sparks on to the ground. Some fall-

146

ing like waterfalls of flame; burnt-out logs glowing redly all over the landscape; branches swishing and falling like torches. It was more like a fireworks carnival than death and desolation, a charred wilderness, with carrion feeding on the fallen stock.'

Sonia Benedict put her fork down quickly. 'You're tired, dear,' she said with a tiny moue of distress. 'You drive yourself so hard. Let Joel and the boys burn off the breaks tomorrow.'

'You'll have to, Joel, in any case,' Ty said levelly. 'I want to bring in that mob from the Jump-Up. I think I'll sell off another five hundred, while they're holding condition.' His voice was entirely without humour. 'Compared to what I've seen we have Paradise here on Koombala. Now we just have to wait for the rain.'

'Indeed, yes!' Sonia said soberly, twisting the beautiful diamond rings on her thin finger. She didn't look particularly well that evening, Paige thought, looking down the table at her. Diane must have thought so too, for her fine white forehead pleated.

'An early night for you, Mamma dear, you were too long out in the garden.'

'I must confess I am a trifle fatigued.' Sonia leaned forward and squeezed her daughter's arm. 'The heat, most likely.'

As likely as this seemed to be, Paige had to dismiss the idea. Ty's news had affected all of them, a horrifying glimpse of what could come. Coffee was served in a little silence with waves of depression lapping at all of them, like water around rocks. When Joel turned his shining blond head to speak to his stepbrother he was making an honest attempt to relieve the tension.

'I'll go down after dinner and line up a few of the

boys to burn off the breaks. We'll start out first thing. Where do you want it done?'

Ty turned his head and the bitterness had gone out of his voice. He began to name off different points of the run while Joel paid scrupulous attention.

Much later on, Sonia put a good-sized whisky and water into Paige's hand and told her to take it out on to the veranda to Ty.

'He's upset about Mundoora,' she explained in a tired, rather restricted kind of voice, her love for her stepson solid and established. 'This may help him relax. He keeps far too much to himself. Always has. He should be able to share a few of his burdens!'

Tracey, who had come up to stand almost at her godmother's shoulder, said in a light, imperious voice:

'I'll take it, Aunt Sonia.'

For once Sonia spoke with asperity. 'I did ask Paige, my dear,' she said with a singular expression.

Tracey didn't speak another word but went back into the living room and buried her head in a book from their latest consignment. Diane, curled up in the shadows of a wing-back chair, already fathoms deep in the latest Desmond Bagley, looked up to take note of Tracey's mutinous expression, then returned to where she left off. In another few minutes she would go and see if her mother had settled for the night. Sonia, though she was the last one to admit it, suffered from a slight heart condition that nevertheless tired her out, but in her daughter she had a most zealous keeper.

With the crystal glass in her hand Paige found her way out on to the veranda. It was a flawless desert night, the stars, in brilliant profusion, gloriously bright.

'Ty?' she said uncertainly. She couldn't see him at first, but caught the particular aroma of his brand of cigarettes.

'Down here!' His voice had a crisp note to it that put her shoulders back. She walked almost the length of the veranda, slipping in and out of the chinks of light that fell through the french windows. He was sitting in a high-backed bamboo chair, his dark head tilted indolently, or seemingly so, blowing wreaths of smoke into the air.

'Well, flower face?' His eyes searched her face, hunting down her motive.

'Sonia thought you might like a drink,' she said, her voice slightly withdrawn.

'Nice Sonia!' he said lightly, and took the glass from her outstretched hand.

Her fingers were still trembling a little from that brief moment of contact. 'I won't disturb you,' she said quickly. 'I realize you're tired!'

It was the wrong answer, it seemed. 'What else do you realize, my disturbing little russet-head?' he asked, lazily mocking.

She went to say something, then changed her mind. His male arrogance and invulnerability was infuriating, hurting her in a way she had never before experienced. 'I know you were avoiding me before you went away,' she said shortly, admitting her knowledge of the fact and not caring.

He took a long sip of his drink, then propped it up at his side. 'So you're not so insensitive?'

Her gleaming head swung towards him. There was no mistaking the shock on her face, the deepening melancholy in her eyes.

'What is *that* supposed to mean?' In the radiant moonlight her face looked ethereal, her cheekbones delicately hollowed.

'What's sauce for the goose is sauce for the gander,' he said idly. 'Besides, I'm damned if I can think of anything better to say!'

Once again as always when she looked at him Paige felt a degree of desperation, the uneasy, tormented desire to be locked in his arms again, lost in a silent green-world closeness. It was as unsought-for a sensation as it was impossible to subdue. She turned away to look over the garden, conscious of his eyes upon her. The night wind, faintly musical, shook out the branches of the trees, swirling spent blossom like a warm current. All around and above them the moon threw out a silvery radiance though which Paige could see a surprising distance. The sandhills were platinum, deep gold in the shadows, upon which, in prick-eared silhouette, stalked a dingo. The wild dog walked to the crest of the hill, then sat on its haunches and howled to the moon.

Paige felt the nape of her neck prickle. 'It seems to sum up the situation, doesn't it?' she asked in a strange, little voice. 'The long-drawn-out hopelessness of it all.'

His voice, when it came, was a deep drawl, spiked with irony. 'If you're talking about drought, honey, rain will fall. I know it!'

'But what else?' she asked lightly, over her shoulder, the tips of her hair curling on to her cheeks.

He shrugged. 'You know, you're dangerous, young Paige. Good at deception. That kind of thing makes a man suspicious!'

She looked down at her slender hands clenched tight on the wrought iron rail, her bright hair curtaining her face. Anything to hide that moment of pain.

'I'll leave you to your suspicions, Mr. Benedict. Good night!'

He was suddenly on his feet with big-cat swiftness, tall and forbidding behind her. 'I'm ready to be bought, little one, but by the right evidence!' he said grimly.

She swung about to face him, finding him much too close, as she tilted her softly cleft chin. 'Do you trust anyone at all?'

He studied her silently for a minute, his eyes moving lightly over her face and bare shoulders, making a jumble of her emotions.

'One or two of my horses,' he said cynically.

'Well, that's a simple, straightforward answer. Even your worst enemy couldn't doubt it!'

A shadow from a moving branch cast a triangle of shade over his face, but his voice had a fine cutting edge.

'Are you my enemy, Paige?

A kind of helpless anger swept over her, compelling her to move a step closer to him. 'I haven't even the comfort of a certain answer,' she said jerkily. 'I just don't know what I feel!'

'*Feel?*' his voice underscored her, vibrant with mockery. 'Now there's an intriguing verb. Almost a give-away. Won't you explain yourself?'

The dark taunting timbre of his voice had her inwardly seething. 'I will not!' she said violently. 'It's my own business, after all!'

'You're wrong about that! It happens to be very much my business too!'

Unbelievably he had caught her off guard. She raised her eyes to him, seduced by a face, a stranger's face, that possessed some special dark grace.

'Oh, please, Ty, this won't help any. I knew I was making a mistake coming out here tonight, to you. You're obviously in no mood for games.'

His voice struck at her forcibly. 'I never play games, flower face. Not ever!'

With an effort she held his gaze. 'You're convincing yourself, not me. I know you're transforming me into someone I'm not.'

All that was formidable and autocratic suddenly left his face. He actually laughed, light out of dark.

'I know what you are, little one. Stay with me and tell me what you are *not*. I could use some entertainment!'

He caught her hand and twisted her back into a shell-shaped chair, watching her like a cat watches a mouse.

'Ty, I think you're crazy,' she said helplessly.

'Who's to blame you? Stay right where you are.' He fell into a chair alongside her, resurrecting his drink.

To have resisted him would have required an effort of will quite beyond her. She stayed where she was, her slender back tilted forward from the waist, one shoulder slightly turned away from him.

'Relax, child!' he murmured with that tantalizing pulse of laughter in his voice.

She let her head fall back, bewitched by the sound of his voice, letting her hands play over the long arms of the chair. He studied her pure profile, the lovely curve of forehead and chin, the faintly tilted, fastidious little nose.

'Either you're a complete innocent or a damned accomplished actress. I'm still working on which.'

'Does it matter?' she asked wearily, shutting her eyes.

'I think so. In short, you present a problem, young Paige.'

'If I do it's one of your own making,' she said softly, her voice laden with insinuation.

He gave a brief laugh. 'I know it! *Trouble*, that's what we're all heading for,' he added tersely.

She opened her eyes, turning her head along the back of the chair towards him. 'You're in a strange mood tonight, Ty!'

His glimmering eyes held her own, setting her adrift in a sea of sharp yearnings. 'Oh, so you know my moods, do you? Coax me out of it. You're woman enough for it!'

'Am I?' She tried hard to be cool and uncaring, but failed.

'Of course!' His voice mocked her, marked by the bright sardonic gleam in his eyes.

She straightened her head again, veiling her eyes. 'It would do me no good to capture your interest!'

'Perhaps not!' he agreed lazily.

The knowledge was too hurtful to be borne. Pain put into her hand the only weapon she possessed. 'It's times like these I'm grateful I'm committed to Joel.'

His chair scraped along the polished floor as he pushed himself backwards. 'That sounds rather Biblical! You're committed, as you put it, to no one. Not yet! I'm correct in saying that!'

The hard conviction in his voice made her defeat final.

'A woman would suffer at your hands, Ty Benedict,' she said tightly, knowing she was suffering now.

'You know better than that!' he contradicted her flatly. 'You've got some good solid thinking to do, little one, before you walk right off the edge. First of all face up to it: You're not in love with Joel. If you were, you'd know it. It doesn't take long. *I'd* know it. We'd all know it. You wear your emotions like a flag!'

It was a moment of falling, of losing her balance. 'And I had the ironical belief my thoughts were my own,' she said bitterly. 'A woman's foolproof reserve!'

She saw the life flare into his luminous eyes. 'Let's test that, shall we? Do you think you could stand it?'

A stupid panic swept over her, stirring up painful emotions. She thought it was tears she was holding back until he twisted her to her feet and tilted her head up, her throat rising like the stem of a flower from her amber silk. He was looking at her from under his heavy lids.

'Please, Ty!' she whispered almost pleadingly.

His voice had a shimmery, destructive quality. 'It's all part of a bad dream, isn't it, flower face?' His wide shoulders seemed to block out the light, a shadow on the moon.

'You're doing this on purpose,' she said a little wildly. 'Trying to get back at me for that very first night!'

A dangerous light flickered in his eyes, then faded in brief seconds. 'Right in one!'

She felt herself go white and lost her head, hitting out at him with a small, clenched fist. Hitting him. Not wanting to hit him at all.

His powerful shoulders shrugged her off. He brought up his hand, securing her wrists and holding them behind her back implacably. 'Take it easy, russet-head!'

She was forced to look up at him, leaning back, staring into his tautened face.

'This sort of thing brings its own penalty!'

She stopped struggling then, her breath shortening, but it was misery more than anything that drove her on.

'Oh, go to the devil!' she said violently.

'Charming!' he laughed under his breath. 'You sweet little innocent! Don't you know some men refuse to be consigned to hell?'

She freed her hands abruptly as his grip slackened. 'Very well then, since you're behaving like a gentleman!'

'It's a lot better than behaving the way I feel!' he murmured with alarming gentleness, and moved back abruptly to lean on the rail.

Everything about him had sharp edges with which to cut her. Paige stared fixedly at him. The moon emphasized the slant of his brows, two bold strokes, the finely concave planes of cheek and temple, the arrogant modelling of his jaw. She would always remember him as she saw him now. Yet he wanted nothing of her but to prove himself right. She didn't love his step-brother. Neither would she make him a suitable wife. And hardest of all to bear was the fact that he was right.

A parrot screeched so loudly that she started, a tremor passing over her, a warning note in the stillness.

155

'I can't stand much more of this,' she said tautly, lifting her hands to her temples.

His eyes slipped over her with ironic amusement. 'Why so dramatic? If I can stand it so can you! Now why don't we raise our spirits and have a drink? Allow me to get you one.' A little smile flickered around his mouth, at once cruel and humorous.

'You're so polite, I'm sure you must hate me,' she said with icy respect.

His low laugh infuriated her. 'Perhaps we should drink to it?'

'Don't bother. I'll go and leave you in peace!'

He was beside her in an instant, a hard detaining hand on her arm. 'Why ever would you want to do that?' he raised his eyebrows in mocking amazement. 'You're stirring up a little life around here!'

'I'll stir up a lot more in a minute if you don't take your hand off my arm!'

'Such abandon!' His eyes had a glittery look, but he only smiled. 'I take it you're threatening me, flower face. Forgive me, my lady, you're perfectly free to do as you wish.' There was swiftly something sardonic in his drawling voice. 'In fact, if I'm not mistaken, here comes your knight in shining armour!'

She half turned away from him, poised in flight. 'You're pretty well armoured yourself!' she said fiercely, then raced along the veranda, swift as a flame, skirt flying, to the comfort of Joel's dazzling grin.

'Now that's what I call a welcome!' he said blithely unaware of the seething undercurrents, coming up the steps two at a time.

A few days later Reg Winton, the buyer for a big

southern syndicate, flew out to Koombala to inspect the five hundred head Ty intended selling off. The bullocks were still holding prime condition and Paige and Di wandered down to the yards before lunch to watch the process of inspection and camp drafting. Ty and the buyer, a thickly set man with a shock of silver-grey hair, stood by the fence while Joel and two aboriginal stockmen rode in among the cattle ready to work a possible reject to the face of the camp.

Joel was looking hot and irritable and Paige flashed him a quick smile of encouragement. He responded at once, a grin on his blond, handsome face. Ty lifted his head briefly to gaze down along the fence, then continued speaking to Reg Winton with an intent, 'don't disturb me' expression on his face. Paige and Di took up a position on the fence, their faces uniformly young and alive.

Instead of milling restlessly, the contented cattle seemed happy enough just to stand chewing the cud, but whenever a bullock was rejected, there was a wild uproar. With a bellow of rage the rejected beast tried to double back to his mates. It was up to the stockmen to press the cunning and powerful bullock back into line. Both girls found this part of the work entertaining to watch and it required a considerable amount of skill on the part of horse and rider.

The horses, at least, appeared to enjoy it, alert-eared, tugging at the bit impatiently ready to outwit the next bullock, for it was an out-and-out contest with horse and rider the inevitable winner. It was obvious that the cattle were well handled, a fact that cost Reg Winton money, but he passed over a big cheque before lunch, seemingly well pleased to do so.

For the rest of the afternoon the men were out on the run, but Joel came back towards late afternoon to take Paige for a swim at the Eight-Mile Lagoon, a favourite swimming place with all the family. It was a refreshing and companionable experience in a beautiful setting, overhung with bauhinias, a pleasant interlude to brighten the day – or it would have been except for a small change of plan: Instead of taking the jeep or the horses, Joel talked Paige into riding pillion on his beloved 'Boney', his Triumph Boneville motor-cycle, a late model wildfire purple machine he sometimes used to muster the stock.

'Chicken' at first, with the normal fear of breaking her neck, Paige found she enjoyed the lightness and freedom of the ride, pleasing Joel with her lighthearted laughter, the wild rose colour that was hers whenever she was happy or excited. It was on the run back to the homestead that fate stepped in – the little things that could alter the course of events. With the family watching in the distance, relaxing in the cool of the veranda, Joel changed gear, turning on a sudden burst of speed leaning hard into a curve. The pedal scraped the side of the track, digging deep into the dirt, then they were rolling, rolling, down the steepish grade with the cycle upended on the track above them, its wheels churning out red dust. Paige felt her body hurtling through space, the sun exploding in a triple rainbow of colour.

She recovered first. She was quite conscious but too stunned and winded to get up. A few yards from her Joel lay supine, his shining head lodged against a small, hump-backed rock that looked like some prehistoric monster.

'Joel?' she called to him, her heart flipping with fright.

There was no answer. None at all!

The jeep raced down the track and ground to a halt beside the motor-cycle. Ty leapt out one side without opening the door and Tracey flew from the near side, giving the door a vicious swipe. She hurtled down the grassy slope, launching a tirade at Paige who sat lily-white and shaken in the deep grass.

'You fool! You fool! It's all your fault!' she raged wildly, furious waves of colour rushing to her cheeks marking her extreme pallor. 'Showing off – all for you! Anything to gain your attention. I hate you. I wish you'd never come out here!' The blue fury of her eyes turned Paige sick. She put a hand to her aching head and gave a soft moan.

Ty came up behind the dark-haired girl, his face grim and forbidding, trying to keep a rein on his temper.

'I'd strongly advise you, Tracey, to keep your mouth shut. As from *now*! Paige is here at Sonia's express invitation. Koombala is *my* property. Paige is our guest and Joel is a reckless young jackass at any time.' There was a honed steel chill to his voice Tracey couldn't mistake. She fell back quickly, faced with a coldly furious ultimatum.

'Are you all right, little one?' Ty's icy green stare measured Paige's face.

'I think so!' she said shakily, touching a hand to her rose-bronze head. 'How is Joel?'

'Knocked cold,' Ty said succinctly, already running an expert hand down Joel's long, lanky limbs. 'No bones broken, and that's sheer luck. Of all the foolhardy stunts!' He sent Paige a lightning glance. 'Stay right where you are. I'll get Joel back to the jeep and then come back.'

After her initial outburst Tracey hadn't said a word, but took up a position beside Joel in the green grass, staring into his white face as if seeking the very mystery of creation.

'So that's how the land lies!' Paige thought with a curious lack of shock. She sat very still, a little crooked smile on her mouth. So that was Tracey's secret – a case of self-interest. Tracey loved Joel and Joel loved Paige and Paige loved . . . no one at all, she told herself unhappily, feeling the first wave of sickness strike. She put her head down quickly.

With much less difficulty than one would have thought, Ty had Joel over his shoulder, moving slowly back towards th jeep. He deposited him gently in the back seat and Tracey got in beside him, settling Joel's blond head against her arm, looking down into his face with a deep, burning anxiety.

Paig turned her eyes away from that little scene, feeling like an interloper. No wonder Tracey resented her! If she cared for Joel with that driving intensity it must have been hell for her watching him lavish his love and attention on another woman. A woman, moreover, who she must have known instinctively didn't return Joel's love at all.

The hot winds of trouble! Paige sat in the long grass with the glorious desert sunset all about her, colouring the world crimson and gold, trembling a little, feeling ready to give way to tears. Ty walked back to her, studying her with a mixture of emotions impossible to describe except that anger was one of them. His long shadow fell across her body and she looked up distractedly, her smoky eyes enormous in her cameo face, brilliant with unshed tears.

'Don't bother with me Ty,' she said raggedly.

'*Now* she tells me!' he muttered quite savagely, picking her up in his arms.

It was then that her body gave up all pretence her mind imposed upon her. She cradled her head against his hard chest, feeling the strong thud of his heart, everything inside her suddenly coming to rest. 'Are you so anxious for trouble?' she asked in a soft, faintly incoherent voice.

He looked down into her pale, creamy face, his eyes very clear, very green.

'If it's got to come, little one, why dodge it? I told you before, you'd have to open your eyes!'

CHAPTER EIGHT

THE drought tightened its grip and the moving of the stock was not unattended by some minor catastrophes; as the grasses around the ever-flowing bores became eaten out, it was necessary to shift the cattle on to other watering places. The danger lay in droving under a blazing hot sun, for thirst-crazed cattle were notoriously difficult to handle. Tempers became frayed, concentration lost, injuries resulting, some of a more serious nature.

Every morning the sun rose as a throbbing red ball and set in phenomenal splendour. Dazzled by its magnificence, it seemed to Paige that had the position not been so critical the sunsets alone made her visit worthwhile, a legacy of the desert proper. A dozen times a day willy-willies spiralled up from the earth, spinning across the plains to snatch up dried leaves and bushes.

The smaller veins of the diminished Georgina, like the Diamantina, were now no longer supplied by the larger arteries disturbing the balance of nature; first in the fish, then in the wild fowl who began crowding the larger lakes in shrieking numbers; jabirus, spoonbills, herons, egrets, and cranes, myriads of pelicans, each fighting and screeching trying to stake out territorial rights.

Then in November, the thunderstorms began. Day in and day out. Night after night. Barbaric spectacles, great towering cloud castles of purplish black that yielded only a silver spatter of rain that evaporated before it reached the parched ground. The anticlimax was almost unbearable. Tempers grew shorter and the natives on the property hard to handle. Paige consoled herself with the thought that she was able to take over many of Sonia's duties as the enervating heat began to cause the older woman physical distress. Even Ty began to look harassed, his dark face stern, insisting on flying Sonia out to her sister in Adelaide, but Sonia refused point blank to go.

'When the rains come!' was all she would promise. Besides, to cement her decision Di and Paige were coping marvellously with the house, the supervision of the staff and the endless correspondence, while Tracey, brisk and competent, took charge of the store and helped on the run. The mutual need had, for a time, created a united front.

Just when it looked as if they were fighting a losing battle, it happened. Sea winds blew cold across the Gulf, deluging *Bogabillain*. Traffic flew between the two stations. Slowly the clouds began to travel in over the tablelands. Rain fell. From the Top End a heavy blanket of cloud spread across the sky, hanging wonderfully low. Surely it held rain! Thunder rumbled and shook the heavens. Light falls were recorded. Nightly the skies were split with great jagged forks of lightning that lit up the grasslands. The rains came down.

Far to the north-west, over a great sweeping arc, rain was falling. Rolling down from the tablelands, teeming in foaming cascades from the ranges, soaking into the plains. Millions of trickles ran into gullies; gullies ran into creeks. The creeks were filling, bursting their banks entering the river heads. The long parched river beds soaked up the excess. The river heads ran faster, stronger over the Outback. Stations, one after the other, went delirious with joy. The natives began smiling, the lubras holding up their skinny babies, tummies distended. All over the drought belt, great winding ribbons of water ran down the river beds; swiftly, silently, faster and faster, gathering momentum.

The Georgina, the Diamantina, the Cooper began to fill up. Over the Territory it continued to rain, a pentup deluge for a land, long denied. The land became satiated, sent down its flood waters to the sixty thousand square mile stronghold of the continent's cattle kings. Hundreds of channels began filling up overnight. Every claypan turned into a lake filled with the sounds of ecstatic wild things.

On Koombala the tension eased miraculously, but not one drop of rain had fallen. Each night they closed their eyes on a sky full of brilliance, the stars radiant and tearless, impervious to Earth's plight.

The rain started in the silent small hours before dawn. Paige came awake, her heart thudding, wondering if it was part of her dream. Let it be rain! Her prayer was as heartfelt as if the land were her own. She flung back the ivory cascade of netting and leapt out of bed, her nostrils assailed by the incomparable scent of damp, steaming earth. She thrust her arms into her almond silk robe and opened out the french doors that led on to her side of the veranda, running out on her bare feet, as wild and excited as the rainbow bird that haunted the reed bed at the creek.

The garden was sporifically fragrant, webbed with diamond drops that glittered from every leaf, every blade of grass. Her heart quivered with fright. The clear sheet of water of the lagoon was cascaded with a million needles of light. Someone was moving across the far end of the lawn; moving with a lithe sureness that became unmistakable. She leaned from the waist against the iron lace balustrade, revelling in the scented spray that dewed her face and her throat.

'Ty! What in the world are you doing?' It was all there in her voice, the heady excitement.

He came quickly across the thick, springy grass. 'Waiting for you, what else?' His black velvet voice matched the night and the rain, faintly exultant. 'This is rain, pretty bird, real life-giving rain. Come on down here and feel it!'

She stood there staring, one hand to her throat, not even trusting herself to speak, uncannily concentrated, filled with an immense elation. In the glittery light he looked like a bronze sculpture, the rain gilding the strong bones of his face, his raven curls crisply curling, settling close to his head in a glossy, rain-silvered cap. There was something wildly exciting, even elemental about the scene – almost a pagan ritual, with a man and a woman worshipping the rain, the night that was mingled with the perfume of wet, tangled greenery; the trees, the flowers, the grasses all shimmering with rain.

'Ty?' she repeated, some of the magic coming into her face, pearly beads of rain embroidering her robe.

'I can't talk to a closed lotus bloom.' He looked up at her, his eyes iridescent. 'A lotus bloom all sheafed for the night!'

The oddly vibrant note in his voice was a shock that

sparked off a bright flame in her. Her heart was beating wildly like a child who had run too fast and too far. Nothing could stop her now. Nothing. She moved as swift as an arrowhead, sure-footed, as graceful as a doe with enormous, shining eyes. She was drenched in seconds, but it didn't matter in the least. Her all-consuming need was simple. An act of sheer recklessness, but a soaring release.

He caught her in flight and pulled her to him, circling her silken, warm body, while his powerful shoulders hid her slenderness from sight. He looked down at her lovely pale face, damp skin and damp hair darkening from rose to bronze in a close gathered stream behind her ears.

'We move on two different planes at once, don't we?' she asked in a strange little voice. 'The only real thing is *you* and your love of playing with fire!'

'Hush!' his hand was on her throat now, the fingers of his other hand curving into her flesh. 'The only thing that ever really matters is *this*!'

The knot of pleasure and pain was blinding. Whatever happened, she thought giddily, she would always have this. She lifted her mouth, counting nothing, her eyes closing, isolated in a magic circle compounded of the man and the night and the rain. Shimmering mists whirled about her head and the world dissolved in a fantasy under his rain-wet mouth.

The thousand-eyed night looked down on them while the rain continued to come steadily in a muffled roar that excluded all save itself.

Somewhere inside the house, a door closed in a deadly quiet protest . . .

Paige dressed in sneakers, cotton slacks, a thin toning shirt in a pale shade of primrose. She brushed her hair. Eyes in the mirror too big, too full of dreams; wish-fulfilment dreams that swirled about in her head like a river in spate. Only this morning she was a riddle to herself no longer. Caught in a corner with no room to manoeuvre, she was forced to face up to the truth. She knew what love was, but she didn't love Joel. Everything she'd done from start to finish was just a desperate cover for her own treacherous heart, a kind of self-deception.

Very soon now, she would have to leave Koombala. Surrender a dream ... make an enemy of Joel. That was inevitable. Her hand trembled a little at the thought. But Joel would survive. Wouldn't she have to herself? She had shown Ty her heart, but he had revealed nothing of himself. Ty was Ty, outside the ordinary laws and rules, but she wasn't going to lay herself wide open to humiliation and defeat. He had thought her a clever actress. She would prove she was one!

She gave a little sigh and turned away. So foolish to make plans, foresee a bright future when there was always the man to topple one's senses like ninepins. She would tell Joel today, a chilling task, but she had already waited too long. Despite her apprehensions a tingling excitement still raced in her veins, but she held herself on guard. The climate of love was slow to dissolve. The muted uneasiness and excitement still persisted like the roar of a seashell held to her ear.

For once from her window the view was obliterated. No crystal blue line of mountain ranges lay in mirage beyond the blunt-nosed sandhills, only a shining, metallic curtain of rain. Down in the breakfast room

Diane had already started on her orange juice. She looked up to smile with real pleasure.

' 'Morning, girl. Listen to that gorgeous rain! Isn't it wonderful?'

'Wonderful!' Paige returned the smile, feeling a quick rush of affection. Di was the perfect antidote to her mood. So full of nonsense, masking a sound common sense, her whole personality meshing easily with the older girl's.

'Where's everyone?' Paige walked over to the warming shelf, with its hot dishes under cover, but she only poured herself a cup of coffee and walked back to the table.

Di pulled a small grilled steak with tomatoes towards her with gusto. 'I haven't laid eye on Ty. Joel had his breakfast early. Tracey should be here any moment. I gave Mother a tray in bed. She said she hardly slept at all for listening to the rain. Lovely task!'

'I got up to have a look myself!' Paige volunteered as she sipped at the strong black coffee.

'Did you now? I just turned over and breathed a great sigh of relief.' Di's greeny-grey glance went past her. 'Hello, Tracey, it's not like you to sleep in. I say, old girl, you look as if you've been pulled through the wringer *backwards*!'

'Thanks!' Tracey's voice was rough-edged.

'I don't mean anything. You just look kind of odd. Everything all right?'

'Don't keep pressing it. I have a headache, if you must know.' Tracey slumped into a chair at the far end of the table, ignoring Paige's quiet 'hello!' Her face was an etching, all sharp hostility. She flashed Paige a chill look of aversion, her firm jaw set, dark circles ringing her eyes.

'Want anything?' Diane asked helpfully, resisting the impulse to pull a face at Paige across the table.

'Just a cup of tea,' Tracey said brusquely, looking down at her hands.

Diane rolled her eyes. '*Thank you, Di,*' she corrected lightly. 'Must mind your manners, old thing, though I don't expect a mite of gratitude.' She got up and poured Tracey a cup of weakish black tea with a slice of lemon, placing it in front of her with an encouraging word.

'Here, drink it up. Guaranteed to soothe the savage breast.'

Tracey made a harsh sound of derision while the other two girls exchanged a look: one of wry humour, the other with a growing sense of disquiet.

Joel chose that moment to make a noisy entrance.

'Good morning, sweetheart!' He dropped a skidding kiss on Paige's cheekbone. 'Morning, girls!' His blond, handsome face had the bright, carefree look of a schoolboy on a glorious lark. He swaggered back on his high boots. 'I've just been out on the run. Every water-hole on the property is running a banker with more to come. The natives are going wild, with the drums and tap sticks going. As Jimmy says: "You plurry beaut!"' He drew up a chair beside Paige and turned it back to front. 'Within forty-eight hours, Red, the desert will bloom. None of your fancy little garden plots but fifty, sixty-mile stretches of wild glory ... the bachelor buttons, the scarlet desert pea, great beautiful clumps of everlasting daisies. It's a sight you'll never forget.'

Amazingly Di's eyes were glossed with tears. She

looked straight across at Paige and blinked a little self-consciously.

'True enough!' she tried to speak lightly. 'When I was a little girl Daddy used to take me out with him to gather all the wild flowers I could carry. He used to put them in my hair, behind my ears, tuck them into my blouse. Everything was such wonderful fun with him. Anyway, he used to say this piece of poetry and I'm going to teach my children the same thing:

"You say we have no beauty in this barren land of ours, no sights to stir the senses, no profusion of sweet flowers.

Have you never seen the verdure that can follow winter rains, or the white and golden glory of the daisy-patterned plains?" '

There was a funny little pulsing silence that Tracey broke.

'You're talking to yourself,' she said harshly with an unexpected tremor in her voice.

'Indeed I'm not!' Di had fully recovered herself. 'Paige, you're listening, aren't you?'

'You know that I am. Your memories of your father must be very sweet.'

Joel got up abruptly and poured himself a cup of scalding coffee, drinking it very fast. 'Well, I have to shove off. Ty wants to clear up some debris brought down by the storm.' He flashed a look at Tracey's white, mulish expression. 'What's with you, this morning? You look all washed out.'

'A headache!' she chopped the words off. 'I'll come out with you. It might go away.'

'Please yourself,' he said indifferently, and swung

back to Paige. 'I'll get finished, then I'll come back in an hour or so. We'll take a run to the Jump-Up. You've got a good view from there. That's if you don't mind getting wet!'

Tracey jumped to her feet, capsizing her chair. A wild kind of anger prowled in her eyes. 'Let's go!' she said forcefully.

Joel turned on her in a kind of amazement. 'You know, sometimes I wonder if you're the full quid!'

'Don't commit yourself, Tracey,' Di contributed laconically. But Tracey had already left the room, her face whitening under the pressure of anger.

'Be seein' you!' Joel shrugged a shoulder and followed Tracey out of the door.

Five minutes later they were hurtling along the track. Tracey was driving, taking the curves much too fast in the rain, skidding in the gravel.

Joel breathed a long-pent-up breath. 'Perhaps you'll tell me what in hell's the living rush?'

Her own breath jagged on her. She changed down, for once grating the gears.

'Come on, Tracey, what's on your little mind? I can hear it ticking over like a time bomb.'

'It's Paige Norton,' she said baldly.

He sat up straight, no slouching. 'Do you think you're qualified to start up that kind of conversation?'

She ignored the extreme sarcasm, turning on him a look that was regretful, compassionate, almost one of pure sadness.

'She's not for you, Joel. Believe me.'

'Would *you* know?' His voice was brash, overconfident.

'I think so!'

He gave a harsh laugh. 'It's no good, Tracey, old girl. You're wasting your time. You know your trouble? You're biased, another word for just plain jealous. That selfish little nose of yours is out of joint. Paige is a big hit. Mother likes her, so does Di!'

'. . . and Ty?'

'I guess Ty likes her too,' he said flatly. 'Now why don't we go back to the house and I'll let you off. You've made your little play, hard and direct. And it was no show at all. I love Paige, I want her, and I'm going to have her.'

'She doesn't want you,' she cornered precariously.

A muscle flicked in Joel's jaw. 'The hell she doesn't! How would *you* know? By the end of the summer we'll be married. You can be bridesmaid,' he tacked on cruelly, grasping at an idea that had been building up in his mind.

She made a funny little noise that was curiously like a sob and ran off the road, pulling the jeep up under the spreading branches of an old man coolibah. She shut off the ignition and turned on him fiercely.

'You'll never see the day. She's in love with Ty. And I can prove it!'

They were glaring at one another, pure hatred in their eyes. 'If you're lying to me,' he said tightly, barely moving his jaw, 'I'll personally give you the whaling of your life.'

'I don't lie!'

He gave a great shout of laughter that was hard and dry. 'That's news! You were the biggest little liar God ever gave breath!'

Her face blanched. 'Not now. Not for years now.'

Something about her white face gave him an odd sense of unhappiness, but anger drove him on. 'So what's your motive? It's ugly, I know.'

'*Ugly?*' She raised turquoise eyes transparent with tears, betraying her driving need.

He thought he would hit her with mingled compassion and rage. She should have been sneering and here she was crying, her face softening into that of a woman's he didn't know.

'Please, Joel, find a way out. She'll only make you unhappy.'

A pulse beat in his throat, visible above the open collar of his raincoat. 'Make *me* unhappy? So you've changed your story already. What about Ty?'

She looked out over the grey world. High up in the coolibah a butcher bird poured out its sweet, silvery song; a hymn to the rain. 'Who ever knows about Ty?' she said sombrely. 'He plays a lone hand. She's very pretty, very feminine. Perhaps he's amusing himself. It wouldn't be the first time. Who could blame him?'

His hand closed over her shoulder with bone-cracking ferocity. 'Say one more word and I'll loosen a few of those nice straight teeth Mother spent so much money on.'

'Lovely!' She shrugged him off violently with strength not inconsiderable in a woman. 'Mummy's little brat all over again. You can't take it can you, boyo? Joel has to have what he wants. Make it up to him for not being the number one son. Well, listen to this, honeybun, you're no Ty. Never will be. He's out on his own, the Crown Prince. Yes, you hate me bringing up one or two of the facts. You're only used to unswerving loyalty from poor silly Tracey who's tagged after you since she was twelve years old. Well, you're still the same spoilt rotten hothead you ever were. Paige Norton doesn't love you. She loves Ty.' She was shouting now, her white face distorted. 'Face up to it, boyo!'

He hit her as hard as he was able, catching the side of her face with his open hand. Ugly red marks spread across the tanned polished skin and tears sprang raw and hot into her eyes, blurring her vision. She collapsed in a huddle, crying as if her heart would burst its confines. He stared ahead, his throat working.

'I'm sorry, Tracey, but I can't help thinking you had that coming. It never pays to pry into someone else's love affair.'

'Not even when I'm forced to stand by and watch you make a fool of yourself?'

'Not even then!' He suddenly bowed his head in his hands and she had the overwhelming impulse to lay her fingers along his cheek.

'I saw them together last night,' she said quietly, forcing herself back to control. 'They were just standing in the rain without even the shadow of a moon between them. I wouldn't lie about something like that. Not when you're tearing my heart out.' She touched his arm briefly and felt his recoil. 'Please, Joel, believe me, I'm only telling you for your own good!'

'That's what they all say, kiddo.' He raised his blond head. 'All the selfless do-gooders, motivated by self-interest. But a pat on the back for a good job well done. The only thing is I don't believe you. I love Paige and nothing you say can alter that. I'll take you back.'

She gave a shuddering breath and pushed open the door, almost falling out on to the grass. 'No, thank you,

174

I'll walk.' He hesitated for a moment, but her temper had reached flashpoint.

'Get! Get out!' she screamed like a fishwife.

'And I hope you fall in the creek!' He swung over into the driver's seat and switched on the ignition. The engine flared into life and he reversed out on to the track, leaving her standing there with tears surging down her cheeks. He didn't know where he was going, so he drove on aimlessly, cursing under his breath tonelessly, monotonously, anything to act as a safety valve on his mounting anger. If Tracey *wasn't* lying! . . .

The origins of intuition are strange. Paige looked up from typing a routine letter to see Joel standing at the door of the study, strange leaping lights in his hazel eyes. She stood up at once and came around the table, the nerves of her stomach tightening. The moment had come.

'Yes, Joel?' she said steadily.

He just stood there, swaying a little, his blond head toffee-coloured in the rain, the skin oddly taut across the framework of his face.

'It's true, isn't it?' he asked, his voice deadly quiet, but the violence was there. Just beneath the surface, ready to gush up. Anything could precipitate it. For a moment there was nothing she could trust herself to say. He walked further into the room, his eyes unwavering. If she'd been a timid woman she would have been shrinking away from him, she thought, feeling only pity for his agonized face. Pity that could blur judgment, disarm resolution.

'I never suspected,' he said tonelessly.

'What, Joel?' The question had to be asked even if it

invited some sort of personal disaster, some catastrophe of the heart.

His face went cold. 'You love *Ty*! Crazily. It's killing me! The thought is killing me!'

Some of her deep reluctance to hurt him drained away. There was anger and bewilderment in his voice, but an underlying strong vein of resentment. She wrenched herself out of her own trance-like immobility.

'No, Joel, it won't kill you!' True or not! Yet how could she deny her love for a man who had made such a devastating entry into her life? The worst was yet to come.

Joel raised sombre eyes to her face. 'So you don't deny it?'

'How can I when Tracey's gone to such lengths to clue you up!'

Anger and tension clung to him like some invidious moss.

'You don't care how I'm feeling, do you?' he cut in with frightening vehemence. 'Just a heartless fraud!'

She flinched a little, her eyes sparkling as most of the colour went out of her face. 'I *do* care, Joel. I'm so very sorry, believe me, but being sorry can't alter anything. If one's secret heart can be fraudulent, then I'm a fraud. I came out to Koombala more than a little in love with you. In love with love, perhaps. No strings attached, you said. But that kind of thing is only good in theory, it rarely works for both sides. I almost wish things would have gone as we planned, but I've discovered it doesn't pay to make plans. They're so easily swept aside. A little loving, Joel, just isn't enough!'

He caught her to him with an anguished groan. 'If

you leave me, Paige, I'll be shot to hell. Ty doesn't want you. He's had any number of women. What's another pretty face?'

Her beautiful eyes were blinded with pain. 'I know, Joel, I know. Don't go on.'

He felt the chill that overlay the warmth of her body. Her hair brushed his cheek and he forced up her mouth to kiss her with a desperate passion.

'Don't despise me, Paige. I can't help it!'

She didn't consider resisting him, with waves of pity ... pity ... sucking her under like a giant surf. He freed her mouth to find the curve of her throat. 'I don't want to distress you, to hurt you, to make you unhappy,' he said with whispered intensity, 'but the facts are recorded. Come with me now. Let's get married, at once. I'll make you love me. I'll work on it like I've never worked on anything before.'

She was breathing with difficulty, leaning back against his arm, one hand in a hard knot at her breast.

'Please, Joel. I can't, I can't!'

The transition from lover to mortal enemy was lightning. He stared down at her with an angry petulance marring his mouth and she covered her eyes.

'I always believed I could take it if Ty took a girl from me,' he reflected. '*A* girl, maybe, but not *the* girl. It's not going to happen.'

'It *hasn't* happened,' she corrected him bitterly, pulling away. 'Though you make it sound like a full-blown tragedy instead of an everyday occurrence!' *An everyday occurrence*, she thought inwardly shaking, more likely the death knell to dreams. 'You have to take it, Joel,' she said hardily, desperately trying to take it herself. 'Take it like a man!'

He glanced sightlessly over her head at the rows of books around the wall. 'I'm not sure I know what that means!' His face hurt her, the tone of his voice. It was so much easier to bear pain than to inflict it.

'I'm sorry, Joel,' she said jerkily. 'I would say it over and over again if I thought it would do any good. I would agonize and sentimentalize or even let you shoot me, but in the end it would achieve nothing.'

Diane's clear young voice, unusually tense, interrupted them.

'Paige? Joel? Is anyone going to tell me what's wrong? Something obviously is.'

Joel threw up his head like a charger. 'Paige doesn't want to marry me.'

Diane seemed to sag against the door. 'I've felt that all along. Mother and I. I suppose worse things have happened at sea. Actually, if you want my opinion, you're not all that compatible in the first place!'

Joel's always unpredictable temper swung againt his sister. 'Oh, go away. Di. We don't want you here!'

'*Paige* does!' she maintained sturdily, her eyes on Paige's stricken face, all her bright colour faded. 'You've got a rotten temper, old son. You always did have. I'm sticking around at least till Ty comes. There's no need to take it out on Paige. She can't help it, you know. These things happen all the time. Just look at her face – paper white!'

The slant of a shadow fell across the hall, then footsteps, and Ty towering in the doorway, his dark face as black and thunderous as Lucifer himself.

'God dammit, Joel, where in hell have you been? I expected you back well over an hour ago. Do you know

I nearly had a bunch drown just waiting for you to turn up?'

'Let 'em drown!' Joel said scrapingly, his eyes blazing with vengeance.

Ty looked as if he could scarcely credit his ears. He crossed the room with shocking speed, getting a hand on Joel's shirt and jerking him round.

'Have you gone crazy or just plain off your head? It's stock I'm talking about. Poor suffering, defenceless beasts!'

The heat was now insufferably clammy with the windows shut against the downpour. Paige wondered why she didn't faint. For half a minute Ty continued to hold Joel motionless, his green eyes glittering like emerald chips, then he suddenly turned his head to stare at Paige as if she had flung him a warning.

'Well, what *is* this?' he asked tautly. 'A lovers' tiff? Because let me tell you, Koombala comes first!'

All at once Joel began to laugh, a wild kind of laugh that held more than a hint of hysteria. 'There you are, sweetheart,' he cried. 'There's your answer. Ty doesn't need anyone. He has Koombala, the beloved substitute.' His face was twisted with misery. He looked young and desperately unhappy. Paige's heart turned in her breast. The vein of compassion that ran so deeply in her almost led her astray. She made a quick, instinctive movement towards him, but Ty held her back against his arm.

'It's now or never, little one. No emotional blackmail. Joel's a big boy now. Either you love him or you don't. Anything less than that isn't fair for either of you. If you love him well and good. If you don't . . . well, he'll recover. Maybe be a better man. It's your decision!'

She felt like raging at him, beating at him with her fists. His dark, imperious face gave her no quarter. She was dazed with the sight of it, moving into a future in which he would play no part. Passionately she shied away from the thought. His arm was a steel bar at her side. Whatever she would have answered was now no longer important, for at that moment Sonia Benedict was making her way along the passageway at a painful run.

'Ty! Ty!' She appeared in the doorway, clutching her side. Not one of them doubted she brought bad news. 'Traffic for Koombala,' she said, her voice breaking. 'Come quickly, Ty, Grandfather Benedict has suffered a stroke – a bad one!'

Ty wheeled immediately, his hand falling away from Paige, almost a renunciation. His green eyes flickered and darkened and in their depths was pain.

CHAPTER NINE

THE first month or so after her return from Koombala had for Paige the unreal, traumatic quality of a nightmare. Every time she stood before her mirror she saw not only her own reflection but that of Ty's, tall and dark at her shoulder, eyes glimmering all the greens of the grasslands. She didn't cry any more, for the initial shock had passed, but an awful constriction would well into her throat.

In those first dreadful weeks of loneliness and longing, she had shunned the night life she had once so enjoyed: the parties, the theatre, ballet, avoiding her friends, who began to worry about her and draw heavily on one another's conclusions, then as the weeks passed she recovered her balance and began accepting all the well-meaning invitations extended with delicacy and tact, more as a peace offering to friends of long standing. But deep in her heart there was grief, distraction under repose, grief for the memory of Ty, who made all the men about her seem pallid, essentially mediocre. Would it always be like that? she wondered, barely registering the fact that unhappiness was making her apathetic towards life.

Her old sparkle was gone, now there was only a cool detachment. But if detachment was content, then she was content at last, cauterized against all emotion, flitting here, flitting there, hunted down by her memories. Her head was immune, icy, numb, but the rest of her body remembered: her heart and her nerves and her blood. 'Big John' Benedict was dead. Ty now reigned in his stead, a powerful man who would, by now, have forgotten *Toongareein*, the rainbow bird, who always flew out by the autumn. Strangely, her work didn't suffer, for she drove herself with a brittle energy, finding a measure of release in the sealed-off hours she spent at her desk or out on an assignment. For the past few months she had enjoyed some considerable success as a freelance fashion commentator compering the dress showings arranged by the big department stores; a job that fell into her hands through her various contacts in the fashion world. Intended, initially, as an emergency standby, Paige proved so competent with her critical, restless intelligence, her natural grace of speech and movement that most of the fashion chain decided to retain her services. In herself, she was proving something of a drawcard, exquisitely groomed, lavishing so much time on her appearance as if her life depended upon it, as indeed it did in a sense; an emotional as well as an occupational therapy. She began to wear her hair longer, experimenting endlessly with clothes and make-up, changing strikingly, becoming in the process an accepted 'beauty' with all that entailed. But cold as an ice maiden, some of her escorts liked to hint, apparently undismayed by the unattainable.

Only once did she break down in the privacy of her own bedroom. She had come home after a long tiring day to find a letter waiting for her from Sonia Benedict with a gently humorous postscript from Diane. They, Sonia, Diane and Tracey, were leaving for Europe almost immediately to catch the first lovely flush of the English spring. They wanted her to know. They would be staying away for possibly six months or so.

Paige read on. They were all most anxious to hear from her. *All?* Paige's softly set mouth began to tremble. Joel had taken over, and very capably, the management of Mundoora from Bob Hilton, who had been moved further north along the chain; both men directly responsible to Ty, who was almost inundated by the pressure of work resulting from his grandfather's death, the winding up of the estate and the reorganization of the Benedict empire. At present he was in Melbourne for an indefinite period. They hoped to see Paige on their return and they would, of course, be keeping in touch with her all along the various points of their stay.

For many long moments after, Paige lay in a huddled heap on the bed. Sadness and despair without concealment, crying as she had never permitted herself to cry since the first dreadful week at home. Then slowly, deliberately, she dragged herself up. Her face would be ruined and she had a morning parade. She had thought she had said her goodbyes and ... forever!

The store was crowded, humming with light laughter and chatter, a sense of pleasurable anticipation, a warm-up for the main business of the morning the 'Autumn Arabesque' a preview of the autumn into winter fashions. This season they were featuring a return to the 'classics' – simple, well tailored clothes, updated with this or that gimmick, a brooch or a scarf or a beret or whatever.

Paige, in an award-winning gown, softly flowing, beautifully cut and pin-tucked, found she had her work cut out. She was bored to distraction with the whole thing ... the trendy background music, the sound of her own voice, the antelope grace of the models, the avid gaze of overweight women with a diet problem. But her voice went on; lilting out the prepared script with a few original touches of her own. A model came back towards her, tall and dark, wide-boned face, grey eyes, her willowy body and delicate legs showing to advantage a superbly cut dress in lightweight wool; a sand beige.

Paige talked her off with sweet fresh emphasis on the V neck and the clever seaming. She bent her satiny rose head to her typewritten copy, seeking out the next showing, her creamy face and throat rising out of her dress like a lily, smoky eyes lifting, only to have her heart shudder and almost stop with pulverizing shock. A tall man, handsome and rangy, powerful shoulders covered by a bronze, summer-weight jacket, moved beyond the periphery of the crowd.

His physical elegance alone would have marked him. She caught the sheen of his eyes, intense and sensually alive, and she faltered and almost broke down. A little ripple of surprise and speculation swept through the front ranks. Tina, the blonde model, gave her a quick, bracing smile of encouragement and she whipped herself back to control her almost buckling knees. The net of gold had reached out to catch her again. It was hard going, fighting out of the mesh that seemed to suffocate her, a throbbing, burning sensation in her breast, her head filled with a million impulses.

At last it was over! She *had* to escape. She was terribly sorry, but she had to escape. In her seeming dementia, she thought she might actually have said *escape.* Jay Warren, the store's fashion co-ordinator, a slick, good-looking Lothario from whom she had always inwardly recoiled, was looking at her rather closely. But his officiousness and deference, the constant barrage of flattery, for once did not go against him. He took charge of her completely; shielding her though the crush with his well-cared-for body, almost breathless with the effort, while her voice, colourless, trembling with unsaid things, contrived to come up with something appropriate. She hadn't been sleeping well, a rushed breakfast, perhaps that was it?

They were going down in the personnel lift and she tried to pull herself together. It was absurd to panic so unwisely. Out in the brilliant sunshine, Jay Warren hadn't the slightest difficulty hailing a cab. He saw her into it with considerable aplomb, then stood back from the pavement smiling her off. She was cruising through the inner city traffic and out to the tree-lined suburbs, the pleasant, inconsequential chatter of the cab driver steadying her, claiming her 'sometime' attention.

She had thought she was over the worst of it; now she was called on again for a tremendous show of strength. The flame had flared up again and a man's face in a crowd sent waves of feeling coursing through her, leaving her weak and shaken. She was running away. Running away from her one and only love. What a joke! She began to laugh and the cab driver looked over his shoulder curiously.

'You know,' he said sincerely, 'I'm not sure if you're not the most beautiful girl I've ever had in my cab. I know your face, do I? On television?'

Paige shook her head and smiled. 'No!'

'Then you ought to be, love,' he chided her.

She was hazy about her directions and they ended up coming the long way round, caught in the seething jungle of Friday's traffic. She felt exhausted and drained when she got back to the flat. Her dress, appropriate to the autumn showing and the property of the store, was far too hot. She undid the tiny covered buttons down to the curve of her breast and walked up the steps to her apartment on the first floor.

The beautiful décor of the small living-room hit her like a benediction, the luxurious hand-woven Chinese carpet. She leaned back against the door and took a long, slow breath, closing her eyes.

A man rose from the deep comfort of an armchair upholstered in greeny-bronze velvet, turning round to face her.

'Paige!'

Her eyes flew open overlaid with violet, points of light standing in the iris. She thought she would fall if she didn't hold on to something. She moved uncertainly, clutching at the back of the long sofa.

'Why did you run away from me?' His eyes moved over every inch of her as if he had every right to so appraise her. 'All to no purpose except to tire yourself out. And that dress is far too hot!' His eyes flickered over the curve of her breast.

She fought her way out of the spell of abstraction. 'Have you the right to question me, really?' Despite her efforts her voice was trembling.

'Wouldn't it be kinder to ask me to sit down?' He returned her gaze with one of equal deliberation.

Some hidden reserve of spirit came to her aid. '*Kinder!* You call this kind, coming here? How did you get in?' Her voice had a rising inflection.

He turned away from her rather casually and stubbed out a cigarette, his lean body rippling with grace.

'The caretaker. I imagine he thought me fairly reliable, and you're not that kind of girl. Very quiet, a lady, is Miss Norton. I have it on good authority.' He was looking at her from under his heavy lashes, green eyes narrowly glimmering. Everything about him was so clear-cut and . . . uncompromising.

'I had a letter from Sonia!' she flung into the void.

'Yes, it was nice of you to let them know how you were getting on!'

She jerked her eyes away from his strange drawing fascination, the hard note of irony in his voice. Did anyone really care how she was getting on? She couldn't believe it.

'They're going to Europe,' she contributed superfluously.

'Of course!'

Why wasn't he moving? she thought hopelessly. Just standing there as if he had all the time in the world.

'How is Joel?' she asked, holding her voice steady.

'Working very well.' The overtones in his voice filled her with a bright, disturbing confusion. 'I don't think he's forgotten you. But he will! Tracey will see to that or die in the attempt. She lacks nothing in will power. These six months are in the nature of a breathing space, for everyone!'

'How nice!' She laughed a little wildly, seized with the strange desire to throw something. 'Aren't they lucky!' Her eyes were brilliant with a kind of defiance, her sensuous mouth quivering. 'Excuse me, I have to change my dress. I'm going out again.'

'You're not!' His voice had a crisp, authoritative note with just the merest suggestion of anger held in check. 'But go and change your dress.'

The stillness of surprise carved itself on her face, her eyes wide and startled. Then her body, too slender, as graceful as a dancer's, went to move past him. The room simply wasn't big enough for him, she could see that at once.

'Paige?'

Something in his voice made her tremble uncontrollably. She paused in the middle of the room, panic-stricken, a haunted, hunted look on her face.

'Come here!'

'No. Not ever. Not ever again!'

He held out an imperative hand.

'Do you like what you're doing to me?' she asked with a wild kind of anger. He was doing it deliberately, making a captive of her. She was swaying a little, tension flaring in her, her eyes seeking an escape route, the hot blood rushing to every inch of her body.

'All right!' he said briefly. 'I'll help you!'

'I'll scream!' Her soft mouth was set with a desperate tightness.

'Please don't!'

The pulse of laughter cut the ground from under her feet. He would always be able to defeat her, rouse this helpless, aching need to know his touch, infinitely exciting, impossible to dispel.

His step was soundless, relaxed and assured.

'Oh no!' she managed to get out. 'Let me go, Ty!' It was a forlorn attempt. Her hunger was too profound. Her shuddering sigh trembled in the air before it was crushed under his mouth. He kissed her with force and passion, holding her head fast, pinning her hand against his heart.

She tried once to turn her head with a pathetically defenceless gesture, but his hand only encircled her softly cleft chin, and then there was no meaning to anything, but a piercing, blinding sweetness, a shuddering magic, a ritual that was known to both of them. She quieted and was still.

When he lifted his head, a flickering light danced in the depths of his eyes and she knew in one instant of time that what she had counted lost had only just begun.

'I love you!' she said, her voice charged with feeling, her pulsing red mouth leaving him in no doubt.

His hands closed over her shoulders with strength and mastery, yet riding his emotions on a curb.

'You do. *Now!*'

She drew back a little, searching his eyes. 'I don't understand you!'

He traced a finger over her creamy pale throat. 'Oh yes, you understand me all right,' he said with wry humour, his manner reassuring her. 'You belong to me, Paige. You have done, right from the first.'

'Then why?' Her eyes focused on him with intensity – seeking the answer. 'Why the past dreadful months?'

A hint of self-mockery flickered over his face. 'Because I wanted you to know your own mind. Far away from the emotional mechanism ... *me* ... where you can't be defeated by ... all this!' His arms imprisoned her, compelling, insistent, and her lashes trembled as he claimed her mouth.

'You're cruel!' she murmured indistinctly.

'If I am, it's to myself!' His eyes were glittering with

a sardonic humour. 'In the middle of a business conference when I was supposed to be making decisions of a sort, I'd look up to see your face. Taking dictation. Answering the telephone. Disconcerting, to say the least. No self-discipline!' His voice was the same yet different, his dark brows lifting, the glow of copper under his skin. 'Now you'll never get away from me. There's no escape, ever. I'm your future and you're my life!'

She looked up at him, recognizing with a sense of intoxicated triumph his strength and mastery, his deeply protective instinct that was so much a part of him, for the first time realizing that his hunger and need matched her own.

A wonderful serenity touched her face.

'It will be the first time the rainbow bird has ever arrived for the *winter*!' she said, her eyes showing a hundred dancing lights, a glow of pride of possession. 'It's lovely, our Heartland. Koombala, our home!' She linked her arms lightly behind his head, but he pulled her to him, his dark face exultant, and all the pieces of the jigsaw fell into place.

A Publishing Event of special interest.

The autobiography of a warm and charming woman who has become one of the most famous authors of romantic fiction in the world

The Essie Summers Story

SEE OVERLEAF FOR DETAILS AND ORDER COUPON